UPSTATE
DOWNSTATE

Folk Stories of the

Middle Atlantic States

by M. JAGENDORF

Illustrated by Howard Simon

Introduction by Henry W. Shoemaker

THE VANGUARD PRESS, INC.

New York

For the Reader

I HAVE traveled up and down and all around five beautiful states—around Empire New York State and diamond-gleaming little Delaware. I have gone through rich, rolling Pennsylvania, abundant, salty New Jersey, and sunny, lush Maryland, and I received a royal welcome everywhere. Wherever I went and said I wanted to hear good stories folks like to tell, a rich treasure of tales was given to me with warm generosity.

I went through shacks, through good comfortable homes, and through royal mansions with stairs wide enough for horses to ride, and every home was opened to me with the same sesame: "I would like to hear from you the old stories you have heard."

In La Plate in Maryland, eighty-two-year-old Mr. Holland Hawkins told me with a twang that can never be put down on paper the tale of the Blue Dog, while a most charming lady living in a house beautiful, high up on the hill, told me another version of the same tale.

In the marshes around Tobacco Stick, Jim, an old Negro sitting on the steps of an unpainted grocery, with yellow gleaming stacks of feed-corn for sale, told me about the White Mule that could not rest until it had done a good deed.

In Delaware a Negro I met walking on the road told me the story of the Fiddler of Fiddler's Bridge. Seventy-five-year-old Mr. Francis Cooch, hale and hearty, living in a beautiful stone house which his wife's family had built around 1735, gave me the story of Fiery-tempered Jake. And Miss C. Maull of Lewes helped me to a rich story in which a blood relative of hers was a participant.

In Pennsylvania an old, retired railroad man, to whom I gave a lift into Port Henry, told the story of the Good Witch-Doctor and Oxenryder who can't rest at peace because he didn't believe in God. A good American with a Hungarian intonation to his speech told me the story of Joe Magerack.

In Burlington, New Jersey, two old men, one without any teeth and the other stone deaf, told me the story of the Pirate and Ann and showed me where the Pirate Tree and the Witch's Tree had stood.

Up in Kingston a grocer told me if I was out on a dry, stormy night I'd see the Phantom Painter trying to finish the painting of the church steeple.

They are just some of those who helped me generously to gather these tales. There were many, many more. Farmers who smelled of the good earth, miners black in face with shiny black clothes coming from the pits. I met butcher, baker, and candlestick-maker; rich man, poor man and lazyin' man sitting around talking and drinking.

And I also met men and women of culture and learning who were more than eager to help me. There was Miss Edith Patterson in Pottsville, who is steeped in mining lore and, of all things, in delightful mining-mule lore. She watches amusedly "her books being written for her." And there are the Shoemakers of Pennsylvania: Colonel Henry Shoemaker, perhaps the first one in America to write what I like to call "folk stories," and who has written more of them than you can count, and Professor Alfred Shoemaker, a folklorist of the purest water, who has the distinction of heading the first folklore department in a college in this country. They all helped me wholeheartedly and with a right good will.

What tales they told me! Each one anxious to show what rich lore there was in his own state, in his own county—in his own neck o' the woods.

There are hundreds of these stories, but, alas, I can only use a few of them—perhaps those that I like best. For this I owe a humble apology to every one of these five royal states—New York, New Jersey, Delaware, Pennsylvania, and Maryland—and to all the folks of these states who love folk tales, and to the many who told them to me. I should have told more of them, but for that I would need thousands of pages and many books. Yet, even if I had written down all of them in many books, I still would not have reached the end. For folk stories born of men's minds, actions, and behavior, are ever appearing like grass and trees and plants from seeds blown by the winds.

I spoke of just a handful of those who told me the stories or helped me get them. I want to mention more of them. Only space forbids me from telling how much each individual person did for me, and I hope they will forgive me.

Before speaking of the folks of the different states I should like to thank collectively all the members of the Historical Societies in every county of the five states. Their help was invaluable. These Historical Societies should really be called Historical-Folklore Societies. They all know both folklore and history equally well. But, then, isn't folklore, in a manner of speaking, folk-history?

I also would like to thank the librarians of Room 300 and Room 328 in the main Public Library of New York City for their great help in getting for me the proper records and books.

Then, in New York State, the following gave time and work: Evelyn B. Britten, of Saratoga; Loring McMillen, of Staten Island; Edward L. Merrill, of Rochester; Blake McKelvey, of Rochester; and, last but not least, Mary Gould Davis, of New York City.

In New Jersey there was Katherine H. Anderson, of Bridgeton; Reverend Henry C. Beck, of Trenton; Mrs. Charles Blake and Mrs. E. L. McConnell, of the Atlantic County Historical Society; Mrs. M. Blauvelt, of Oradell;

Kathryn P. DuBois, of Maywood; Hon. Hugh L. Mehorter, of Woodbury; Charles E. Moreau, of Bloomfield; W. C. Mulford, of Bridgeton; Miss Lizzie J. Price, of Burlington; Joseph Sickler, of Salem; Mrs. Marion B. S. Weatherill, of Woodbury; Mrs. Aline K. Wolcott, of Riverton.

In Delaware I owe particular thanks to Ruthanna Hindes, of Wilmington; Mrs. Bertha M. Carrow, of Saint Georges; A. O. H. Grier, of Wilmington; Freddie Lloyd, of Saint Georges; Mr. Leon de Valinger, Jr., State Archivist of Delaware; Miss Mary E. Weber, of Christiana; Miss Catharine C. Maull, Curator of the Zwaanendael Museum of Lewes.

In Pennsylvania I owe much to Mrs. Adelyn Keffer, of Harrisburg; Horace Mann, Curator of the Doylestown Museum; Mrs. Jane K. Burris, of Norristown; William S. Troxell (Pumpernickel Bill), of Allentown.

In Washington, D.C., to Mrs. Maidy Campbell, who dug up old records for me.

In Maryland, tales and records came from Mrs. William H. Beach, of Public Landing; Dorothy Elderdice, of Westminster; W. Holland Hawkins and Mrs. Carlos Gravenberg, of Port Tobacco; Mrs. Ethel B. Hayden, of Baltimore; Mrs. Jeanne MacGlashan and Mr. A. A. MacGlashan, Sr., of Plaindealing; Mrs. F. W. Mish and Mrs. Fanny E. Pennington, of Hagerstown; Mr. J. W. Foster and Mr. Frank F. White, Jr., of Baltimore.

And, finally, I owe no end of thanks to Sophie Jagendorf, who did the hardest chore in the library, wading through records and catalogues and books. Last, but not least, there is Nancy Hosking, who watches that I cross my t's and dot my i's, and many more things besides, and Evelyn Shrifte, who helped unstintingly to edit the book.

M. JAGENDORF

Old Cole Farm
Carmel
Putnam County, New York

Contents

Illustrations

BOOKS BY M. JAGENDORF

PROSE

New England Bean-Pot
The Marvelous Adventures of Johnny Darling
Tyll Ulenspiegel's Merry Pranks
A World of Stories for Children (IN COLLABORATION WITH
   BARRETT CLARK)
In the Days of the Han

PLAYS

Penny Puppets, Penny Theatre and Penny Plays
One-Act Plays for Young Folks
Pantomimes for the Children's Theatre
Fairyland and Footlights
Nine Short Plays
Around America with the Indians (IN COLLABORATION
   WITH NINA B. LAMKIN)
Plays for Club, School, and Camp
Buffalmacco's Jest
The Pie and the Tart (ADAPTATIONS)
The Farce of Pierre Patelin
The Cave of Salamance
Jeppe of the Hills
The Pastrybaker

ANTHOLOGIES

Twenty-Five Non-Royalty Plays for Children
Twenty-Five Non-Royalty Holiday Plays
Twenty Non-Royalty Mystery Plays
Twenty Non-Royalty Ghost Plays

IN PREPARATION

Folk stories from the Southern States
Folk stories from the Southwestern States
Folk stories from the Northwestern States
Folk stories from the Western States

Foreword

I THINK that Stephen McKenna made about the best definition of folklore: "Isn't superstition only a belief that one doesn't hold oneself?" This, the collection of the Middle Atlantic States' folk stories, is the latest and easily the best of the books published by Dr. Moritz Jagendorf. In it he presents folk tales that cover all ways of life, all manners of livelihood. From New York, Delaware, New Jersey, Pennsylvania, to Maryland, and to Washington, D.C., the volume covers more than mere territory, even as the ways of life and manners of livelihood, geography, and race-culture affect folk tales.

These are the tales of farmers, of fishermen, of hunters, of sailors and pirates, of judges and of governors. They are the tales of housewives and of storekeepers, of millers and of ministers. They range from the serious to the humorous to the thoughtful, and from the ridiculous to the philosophical. They are the stories and the lives of all people, written for all people in the simple language all can understand. As McKenna says, "When you get fifty miles from a railway, you're in a different country, and a different century."

When we think of folk tales, we conceive of a thing that is a fairytale only. But this is not true. A folk tale can be a simple narrative of a real happening or it can be of historical value, as of government and systems of governments. Folklore often indulges in the supernatural, in the hechs, hobgoblin, and "deil." Other tales are simple yarns, exaggerations but to amuse. Then there are the tales that teach morals, simple lessons which are the main type told by our ancestors in the Old Country.

In this volume Dr. Jagendorf has written in the charming manner of the Old Country way of telling tales. He has the spirit of childhood, and at the same time his own mature wit and humor dart here and there in laughter. A quiet good thing is his philosophy, explaining the inner meaning of many of the tales.

Presented here are the folklore tales of a section of America, a rich heritage of the young, who, having left the Old Country behind, absorb the culture of the new, and which will strike a light in every native child's consciousness—stuff that can never be forgotten once absorbed, giving every child and every adult a spiritual impetus in the reading.

What are the "best" chapters? Well, they are all "more than good." Of particular interest in the collection is "Bees In The Bonnets," a New Jersey folk tale that flows so with rhythm it seems more a song than a tale. "In Coney Island By The Sea," is a New York tale which represents New York City as seen by children all over the country. A favorite tale of Maryland is the "Cookus,

Bopple, and Yeakle" one, depicting the value of common sense.

Far the favorite of the Pennsylvania tales is "The Great Sacrifice," a legend surrounding George Washington. A wondrous legend, it is the story of a brave Pennsylvania German girl, the daughter of a Tory inn keeper at Brickerville, who plotted against the life of the great general. Sympathetic to the American side and having learned of her father's plan to murder the general, the girl Elizabeth ingeniously takes the general's place in his room at the inn. Her purpose was successful, and she was murdered unknowingly by her own father. It is a sublime story, and leaves a profound impression on the reader.

Upstate, Downstate: Folk Tales of the Middle Atlantic States *is among the best in American Folklore. Our folklore has come to its full ripeness of understanding, and can be collected freely. Dr. Jagendorf has shown in this book how it can be done at its best.*

State Museum
Harrisburg, Pa.
August 30, 1949

HENRY W. SHOEMAKER
President, Pennsylvania
Folklore Society

NEW YORK
The Empire State

Mighty Mose, the Bowery B'hoy

OH, New York City is a mighty great city, the mightiest great city in all the land. It's got the biggest houses and the most people, and once it had the strongest man that ever was, and his name was Mighty Mose.

You can hear all about Mighty Mose in Old McSorely's, a grand old place in New York City, where men sit around wooden tables with golden ale before 'em, talking only when they have something to say. You can hear about him, too, where men come for a night's lodging along the wide street from Cooper Union to Chatham Square.

He was a grand sight in little old New York, was Mighty Mose. He was a fireman, the finest fireman who ever wore a red shirt with white pearl buttons. Folks say he was seven feet tall and had arms hanging down below his knees. His hands were big as the ears on the elephant in Barnum's Circus, and on his big dogs he wore shoes large as canal boats coming down the river.

That Bowery B'hoy wasn't scared of Old Nick and

3

his black-tailed tribe, nor of all the toughs in the "Plug Uglies," "Five Points," or "Dead Rabbits," the gangs of New York that were the roughest gangs in all the world.

One sunny morning Mighty Mose, jaw stuck out, pants rolled up, was walking down the Bowery with Syksey, his shadow and best pal.

Mose's hair was red as a burning brush. He wore his red shirt with white pearl buttons, and he looked like the salt of the earth. On his red hair stuck a three-foot-high stovepipe hat with thick black crepe around it, and in his mouth stuck a two-foot cigar, smoke coming out thick as clouds. From one side of his belt hung a butcher's cleaver, and from the other, a good-sized barrel of golden ale.

'Twas a beaut of a morning, with the wagons rumbling and people shouting while the two walked to the shining Hudson River.

"Mose," said Syksey, "Mose, I heard Jim Jeroloman's gonna have a muss with y' t' keep y' from goin' to the fireman's ball with yer gal Liz. That feller's too big for his leg-panties."

"Honky Tonk," sang out Mighty Mose. "Is that so? Big Jim, the chief bully of fire engine Live Oak No. 44, is a strong b'hoy, but our engine, Lady Washington, is finer than his, an' I'm stronger'n twenty Jims put together. Betch y' I'll beat 'm in a fight without a single blow—an' he'll eat hay out o' me hands."

"Don't bet nothin against y', Mose, if y' say so I knows

y'll do so. Why, Mose, I thinks y're so bright y' kin use yer hand fer a lookin' glass."

Came along the street Dirty-face Jack, Scar-faced Orange County, and Jim Hurley, the Sweet Singer of the Dry Dock. All had heard that Six-foot-four Jim with gold earrings was going to have a muss—a regular fight with Mighty Mose, and they came to see the fun.

"An' where may ye be goin', big Mose, early in the mornin'?" said Orange County in a great voice. "Heard Jim Jeroloman'll keep y' from the fireman's ball."

"Maybe he will an' maybe he won't, but now I'm gonna have a little workout t' get ready fer 'm."

They came to the docks of the glimmering Hudson full of boats going and coming.

Said Mose, "What would y' like to see me do? Hop across from Manhattan t' the Jersey side with a single jump, or swim across the river with two single strokes? Two single strokes across to Mosquito berg an' two t' come back to Manhattan Isle."

Dirty-face Jack was for the mighty leap, but Orange County and Jim for the grand swim.

"First I'll tune me lungs up a little," said Mose.

The *Britannia*, a mighty British ship, came into clear sight then. Mose took three deep jumbo puffs on his two-foot cigar, and his chest came out three feet high. He let out smoke thick as fog, and a roaring breath that flung that British ship full three miles out to sea.

Mighty Mose and the bullies in their red shirts roared with laughter.

Then Mose cried, "Now I'll show y' the way a real Bowery B'hoy makes ready for a muss."

He handed his two-foot cigar to Syksey and said, "Hold de butt."

Then off came his red fireman's shirt. Next he unhitched the keg of ale, threw it on the grass, and crying, "Drink to me health," he leaped into the water.

Syksey, Dirty-face Jack, Orange County, and Jim the sweet singer, watched with open eyes.

Mighty Mose took only two giant strokes, and there he was on the Jersey side. In he dived again—two more mighty strokes, and he was on the New York side.

Mose came out and shook himself like a poodle dog. He put on his clothes, put on his stovepipe hat, and they all went swaggering down the Bowery.

When they got to Chatham Street, there was Six-foot-four Jim Jeroloman leaning against a lamppost, a cigar stuck in his mouth and a plug hat on his head. On his red shirt, "Live Oak No. 44" was embroidered in purple silk, and from his ears hung two shiny gold earrings. His broad pantaloons were rolled up, and he wasn't going to a fire, either. He was in a grand mood for a muss—just a little sporting fight to keep Mighty Mose from going to that fireman's ball.

As soon as he spied Mose he shouted:

"Y're bigger 'n I am but y' ain't stronger 'n I am. I ain't scared o' y'. Come, let's have a muss, a knock-down-an-drag-out t' see who'll take Liz to the fireman's ball tonight."

A great crowd had come around 'em.

Mighty Mose just laughed and laughed, showing his gleaming teeth. Then he said:

"Jim, I know ye're a great slugger an' a gouger an' a hobnail stamper. An' I also know y're the chief bully of Live Oak No. 44, but my fire engine Lady Washington No. 40 is a fine engine, too, an' we need a good new brakerman. I'll not muss wi' y', for I wouldn't hurt y' for anythin'. Tell y' what, I'll show y' a trick I kin do, an' if y' do the same, I stays away from the fireman's ball. If y' can't, I take Liz, an' ye join up with me engine."

Jim, he couldn't say no, too many were listening, for the great crowd around 'em had grown bigger and bigger.

"I kin do anythin' yuh kin do," he said, bragging.

A streetcar full of ladies and gents, drawn by two big white horses, was coming down the tracks. Mose went up to the lamppost where Jim was standing and tore it out with one good pull. The horse-car was right near, so he put the lamppost under the bellies of the horses widthwise and put his giant hand under it. Then he placed his left hand under the trolley and raised up those two horses and the car full of quaking ladies and gents. Raised 'em right up in the air just as if they were a penny toy.

Horses and trolley, ladies and gents high in the air, he began walking down the Bowery. A great crowd of Bowery b'hoys and g'hals and others followed them. There was cheering, hoorahing, and whistling like for a big show. And a big show it was, with Mighty Mose the

Bowery B'hoy showing the full strength of his arms, carrying a horse and trolley high above his head like a child's toy.

When Mose came to Grand Street, he put down the quivering horses and quaking passengers and turned to six-foot-four Jim.

"Now, Jim" said he, "do the same 's I did, just as we agreed. Carry back that streetcar, horses an' driver an' ladies an' gents, right t' Chatham Street."

Jim shook his head with the dangling earrings an' said he couldn't.

Said Mose, "I wins. Since y' can't, y' must join our engine, an' I takes Liz to the ball."

Mighty Mose went to meet his gal Liz. They walked to a fine restaurant on Grand Street, sat down, and Mose sang out:

"Waiter, gimmie two six-penny plates o' po'k an' beans an' don' stop t' count dem beans—d' y' hear!"

When they were done, they took a horse and buggy and raced up the Post Road till Liz's hat near flew off her head.

She braced her feet against the hard footboard, and Mighty Mose roared:

"Liz, 'tain' graveyards we're passin', it's milestones, an' when we come back we're goin to the fireman's ball. Yuh an' I, for a grand old time."

And a grand old time they had.

The Devil
and the Good Book

OH, the Devil came to Sheepshead Bay
And tried to carry some Sheepsheaders away,
but he could not do it, and this is the reason why.

Around Sheepshead Bay, between the waters an' the swamps, there lived good folks, some colored, some white, at peace with each other an' all the world. They worked an' they fished, ate greens, potatoes, an' what the sea gave 'em free, an' life was sunny an' singin' just like the water in the bay, until one fine day when somethin' went wrong.

The minister, in his black coat, was sunnin' himself, the elders were around talkin' 'bout the Lord in Heaven an' people on the earth, when there came up a man an' his wife who lived at the end of the town.

"Minister an' elders," the man said, "my house's conjured. There's evil spirits roamin' around our home an' hearth. Every night there's queer noises 'nuf to frighten even the cat, an' my wife an' I an' children are frightened, too."

"Have y' seen the roamin' spirit?" the good preacher asked.

"No, we haven't, we're afraid to go out into the black night, but you kin see hoof marks early in the mornin' in the swamp an' grass, an' sure 's turnips them's the Devil's footsteps. Y' kin see his cloven hoof marks clear 's a silver dollar in the moonlight."

The minister an' the elders, they got up an' walked right where that man lived. Sure 'nuf, there were hoof marks full clear 's for anyone to see.

What to do?

There was high talk an' argufications, an' talkin' up 'n' down n' all around. Then preacher an' elders said they'd hold a prayer meetin' in the bewitched house of the man an' drive that Devil away with song an' prayer.

Came night. Kith, kin, an' caboodle, neighbors an' friends as far as Coney Island by the sea, they all came to that prayer an' song meetin'. Halleluja!

The stars, they danced their shiny dance in the sky, an' a sliver of a moon came out bashful-like, but the good folks of Sheepshead Bay, they crowded into the little cabin of the man that had a bewitched house.

Preacher began to preach, told about the good folks in heaven an' how folks on earth could get there, too. He preached mighty long an' quoted the Bible about Abraham, Isaac, an' Jacob, an' all the saints who loved Jesus. Then they sang about the Lord an' his angels.

Preachin', singin'; singin', preachin'; it went on a long, long time, with handclappin' an' shoutin' in between.

Of a sudden the woman who lived in the house cried: "I hear footsteps comin'."

The singin, an' preachin' stopped dead. Preacher, elders, an' congregation listened with all their ears.

Sure 's jay birds, there was heavy footsteps outside like some wild beast runnin' an' tryin' t' git in the house but held back by the holy songs an' prayer.

Them footsteps was comin' nearer . . . everyone in that cabin stopped breathin'.

Now . . . now . . . there was horns peepin' in through the boarded little window. . . .

"Get thee hence, Satan," preacher roared.

But the horns just kept maulin' around, tryin' to break through an' maybe come in an' catch some innocent soul to drag it down below.

Preacher kept on prayin', horns kept on borin'. Then preacher raised the Good Book in his hand an' cried:

"Here's all the good words in the Bible, Satan, y' can't resist that!" an' flung the Good Book right at the horns. Prayin' men an' women threw their books right after it, an', Halleluja! the horns stopped borin' an' soon were out o' sight. There was a swishin', trompin' noise, an' then all was still!

Preacher waited, mumblin' prayers, then he opened the door slowly. . . . There was nothin' to be seen! All you could hear was a tree toad peepin', bullfrogs bellowin', and whippoorwills callin' their names.

Preacher an' congregation, they all came out, an' there

in the dewy grass y' could see, even in the dark, the hoof marks of the evil spirit.

Preacher set up a great prayer, an' congregation joined him, singin' the praises of the book of the Lord that was strong enough to drive the Devil away just by touchin' his horns. From that day on

> Devil never came to Sheepshead Bay
> Tryin' to carry Sheepsheaders away.

The Tale
of Anthony's Nose

FROM the year one, New York City, first called New Amsterdam, was full of great men who did marvelous deeds. But there was one who was greater and did more marvelous deeds than all the others, and his name was Anthony the Trumpeter.

Anthony the Trumpeter was greater than the greatest, for he was as round as he was tall, which no man ever was before. When he walked in the streets or in the country, or rode on the lordly Hudson River, he was a grand sight to see, and the grandest of all was his huge, thumping nose sticking out from his face. It was a nose fit for poets to make songs about. It was long and thick and red and rosy. It shone like St. Elmo's fire and could be used as a lantern on dark nights.

Anthony's voice was fully equal to his nose, and when he blew a blast on his brassy trumpet it was heard not only up and down and all around New Amsterdam but up and down and all around the Hudson River.

For all these reasons he was the right-hand counselor

of Silver-leg Governor Stuyvesant of New Amsterdam, who sent him wherever there was weal or woe.

One day the governor with the thumping pegleg sent Anthony the Trumpeter up the Hudson to the Wilt-wyck Fort on a grave mission of state.

He went on a boat round like himself, and they sailed slowly up the river, eating and drinking and making merry, as good Dutch burghers of those days were wont to do. So they came to the Dunderberg.

The good Dutch captain took no chances with the goblins of the place who could let wild winds loose. He lowered the mast and even bowed his own tall hat to show the proper respect to the keeper of thunder, lightning, and winds.

For that reason the waters remained calm, and the air was sweet around the Dunderberg and the mountains on the opposite side.

The shipmaster dropped anchor right at the shore of the mountain across from the Dunderberg. Then the good Dutch sailors and Anthony the Trumpeter, lord of the finest nose in all the land, ate and drank and talked and slept peacefully.

Early in the morning Anthony arose. He was hungry, as any man would be after not eating for a long, dark night.

He washed his face in the warm water of the river and dried it with a rough Dutch towel till it glowed and gleamed like the copper kettles hanging over the Dutch ovens.

Then, with nothing else to do but wait for a good breakfast, he hung his face over the rail to watch the dancing fish, blue, gray, and green, large and small, playing joyfully in the glittering water.

Right then Master Sun came up over the mountain, large and fiercely gleaming.

The sun loved Anthony's nose more than any other man's, for it gleamed like his own radiant face, and so he shot a most powerful, gleaming, glowing flash of greeting to it.

Then something happened that had never happened in this world before.

The fiery dart of the golden sun and the red glow of Anthony's nose together made a streak of lightning greater than was ever seen in the land. That streaking, fiery snorter fell like a fallen star into the Hudson River and struck a giant sturgeon that was playing in the water.

Even if that sturgeon had nine lives like a meowing cat it would have done him little good. Nothing in all the great world could withstand the power of the lightning made of gleaming sunshine and gleaming Anthony's nose.

That sturgeon was broiled so fine and crisp that even the wet waters of the Hudson could not soften it. Quickly, good Anthony hoisted the fish out of the water, and captain and crew and the great Trumpeter, with his heavenly nose, sat down to the finest feast ever served.

It was the very first time men in the new land ate

broiled sturgeon, and it tasted like manna in this happy wilderness.

It tasted so good that Anthony and the captain thought it more important to return at once to New Amsterdam and tell the governor about their new, fine, eating fish than go on their mission of state to Wiltwyck Fort. With hook and line and nets, they set to work and caught a mess of sturgeon and turned back their round boat to Amsterdam town on the tip of Manhattan Island.

When the governor tasted the broiled fish he said that Anthony was right in turning back, for the flavor of this new fish was more important than the most important matter of state. And to commend him for his wisdom for the rest of time, the governor named the mountain where the new fish was found and broiled by a streak of lightning from Anthony's nose—Anthony's Nose.

Anthony's Nose it has been called ever since that day, and a good name it is.

The Phantom Painter
in the Steeple

WHEN men worked and walked with ease and life was very simple, there lived in Kingston on the Hudson a dominie and his wife.

The good dominie loved traveling as much as preaching, and so he often went down the river to New York City, the gay city, to see what he could see. After such trips his sermons were better and longer than ever, and that made the good people of Kingston better fit for heaven, though they liked very much to stay on this earth awhile.

One time the dominie went to New York City and took his goodwife along. When they had their fill of food and pleasure they boarded the round-bellied sloop and turned back to their home on the Hudson for preaching and quiet living. There were other burghers on the boat, and cattle and goods as well, and all sailed slowly up the Hudson along the green palisades, at peace with all the world.

So they came past the Dunderberg, the Thunder

Mountain from which winds, thunder, and lightning came over the hills and over the valleys and over the little farms that were all around. Of a sudden the good-wife of the dominie let out a terrible screech that could be heard clear to Albany. It frightened even the Indian savages on the shores. Her round face got red to bursting, and she stared straight before her, pointing to the bowsprit of the sloop. There sat a thick hobgoblin, dressed in green cloth just like any Dutchman, eyes bulging out a full inch, mouth wide as a tub, and ears big as owl wings. On top of the ears was a long, peaked cap ending in a point. 'Twas a face enough to freeze a river on a hot summer's day and make children hide their heads under feather quilts.

The dominie, the captain and the crew, and the other passengers, and even the animals, turned their faces to where the goodwife of the dominie pointed, and their breath stuck fast in their throats.

But the dominie was a holy man and knew full well how to tackle evil spirits.

First he began singing a song in praise of Saint Nicholas, then he chanted Latin words that would drive the arch-enemy to the end of the earth.

The hobgoblin knew he had to go. He yowled with passion and screamed with fury. He roared with anger and made faces to turn men into stone. But the dominie kept up his exorcising chants, and in the end the evil spirit had to fly away or be destroyed. He flew off straight toward Esopus, or Kingston town, and was soon out of sight.

He flew high in the air, swearing vengeance on the dominie who spoiled his game, until he came to the old church where the dominie preached and prayed.

Around the church he flew, around and around and around, figuring just what to do to teach the dominie a lesson. In the end he decided the best thing was to fly into the church, hide, and spoil the Sunday sermons.

He circled wildly around the slender steeple, trying to find a way in. But a wind came along, took off his cap, and flung it onto the highest point of the spire, where it stayed. Right then he saw a little window open below. He ordered his cap to wait for him and squeezed in through the window.

In the church he walked around the benches and around the altar, for he had never been in a house of God before. Then he turned the benches over, threw the Holy Book on the ground, and did whatever mischief he could. When he was done, he flew up the window to get out and found he couldn't.

The holy place and the harm he had done held him prisoner. He flew around and around, but, no matter how hard he tried, he could not get out.

The sloop with the dominie, the captain, the crew, and the people, came into the bay. The good man of God and his little round wife went to their home that was near the old church. They said their prayers and slept the sleep of the good, never dreaming of the mischief the hobgoblin was doing in the church.

Betimes the next morning they were awakened by a crowd of good burghers of the town who were standing around the church, heads and noses high in the air, pointing to the slender steeple.

The dominie and his wife rushed out, looked upward and saw on the top of the spire—the peaked cap of the goblin of the bowsprit!

The dominie crossed himself and shouted a Latin prayer, and one in Dutch as well. But all the praying wouldn't get the cap off. Young folks tried to climb up, but with all the trying the cap would not come off. For that peaked cap had to stay there until the hobgoblin would take it off himself. No one in the town liked this.

And that was not the only thing the burghers didn't like from then on about their lovely church. There were other things besides.

There were strange noises on Sundays, never heard before. Some said it was the snoring of the rich, but this was not true. The dominie knew it was the hobgoblin there to spoil his long sermons, so the worse the noises, the longer the sermons, and the dominie won out every time.

Time went on with the peaked cap on the church outside and the weird noises inside, until wind and weather, snow and rain, took off the paint of the good church and it needed a new coat of white paint.

Master painters came from all over, looked at the church, but when they saw that goblin cap on high, said they were afeared to paint, for it was too high and they might lose their holdings on the scaffold. At last one man came along and said he was not afraid of cap or height and would do the work.

The painter, tall and thin, with deep-set eyes, went to work. He built a fine high scaffold and as soon as it was done began painting.

Day in, day out, he painted patiently, going higher all the time, getting nearer to the window through which the hobgoblin had come.

One day the painter painted the day long, and would not stop, though the sun was setting golden red and the sky was green like the sea and the church inside was dark and dim.

The sun sank down behind the green hills, but the painter was still painting. He was now right up to the little window.

He turned his face, looked at it, and reeled back clutching the wooden rail!

There was a face in the window that looked like the end corner of hell. It made his heart stand still.

It was a terrible face, with eyes standing out as long as a fist, mouth wide as a barrel, full of green fangs, cheeks puffed up thick as a frog's, and hair red and black and matted, with two ears stuck out like a dirty owl's wings. The ugly face was full of hatred and anger, enough to make time stand still.

He saw it but for a moment, yet it was enough to put him into an icy sweat, and he tottered from the scaffold.

He walked home counting his steps and went to bed. He never got up again and never finished his task.

The day he died and the bell tolled in the little white church for him, the hobgoblin's cap was no more on the steeple and the hobgoblin was no more in the church. For the death of the innocent painter caused by the goblin's face had given the imp the power to escape from the holy place, and he was never seen or heard from again.

But on wild and windy nights, when the ice floes come down the Hudson, folks coming from warm and welcome visits and going past the Old Dutch Church see the figure of a tall, thin man with hollow eyes painting wildly and fiercely, trying to finish the work he left undone.

In Coney Island
By the Sea

WHEN Polar Bears and Icebergers get talking up in Stauch's Solarium in Coney Island by the Sea, tales come flying like snowflakes on winter days.

Let me tell you I'm not speaking about wild beasts in the icy Arctic. I'm speaking of men and women, boys and girls, short and tall, thin and fat, who love the ocean so much they go swimming all year round, New Year's and Christmas, too, at Coney Island by the Sea.

I want to tell you one story I heard from Mike McGrath, the rollicking Irishman from Featherbed Lane who was a grand storyteller.

We'd sit around mountains o' sandwiches and heaps o' bottles waiting to take a dip, while from down below came the smells o' popcorn and hot dogs, the music of carousels, and the screeching whistles of the loop-the-loop. There was shouting of barkers, too, and tramping and talking of millions o' people on the boardwalk, and, over everything, the never-ending pounding of the sea.

24

They were grand noises. Mike 'd join 'em, bellowing loud:

> "Me Mither an' Father was Irish,
> Me Mither an' Father was Irish,
> Me Mither an' Father was Irish,
> An' I'm Irish, too."

When the song was done a tale 'd come.

"D' ye want a story o' Coney Island's Red Leary and Red Kate his wife, who rescued him from prison while a might o' men were watchin' close? Or d'ye want t' hear about Jim Brady all covered with diamonds so you couldn't get a glimpse of his shirt?

"Or maybe you'd like t' hear about the goofy doin's of the queer folks in Steeple Chase Park or Luna Park; 'bout Zipo the pinhead, or the fattest woman in the world, or the thinnest man.

"Here's one. Mebe you'd like a story of the greatest animal trainer that ever was in this whole world, who could keep twenty-seven wild lions quiet by the mighty power of his eyes. That was Captain Bonavita of Coney Island.

"He was a great man indeed, but one time something funny happened to him even though he was a great man. I'm goin' tell you about that.

"One evenin' he went visitin' his darlin' Marie to take her to Luna Park to see him for the hundredth time goin' into that iron cage with twenty-seven lions waitin' on gilded pedestals.

"They came to the grand theater where people sat in

the glarin' lights thick as flies to see the great man who could frighten twenty-seven lions with his eagle eyes.

"Marie, she was right in front to watch the man she loved doin' his darin' deed.

"There was the cage, white an' gilded, an' in it sat the twenty-seven lions on scarlet an' golden tubs while a band played grand music. Then the musicians stopped, except the drummer man who kept on beatin' the skin. Then he stopped, too, an' it was so still ye could hear a sigh.

"In came Captain Bonavita with curly black hair, waxed handlebar mustache, an' black eagle eyes. He wore a bright red military coat covered with medals an' a large flower on 't. In his hand he held a short whip. There was a man to set a woman's heart a-flutterin'!

"He opened the door o' the cage, walked right in between the twenty-seven lions without winkin' a lash.

"The great crowd watched, eyes an' mouths open, holdin' their breath.

"Suddenly—Saints preserve us—a terrible thing happened! One of the lions became a little jumpy an' began roarin'. Captain Bonavita raised his hand, an' the animal leaped at 'm, sinkin' her teeth deep in his flesh! There was screamin' an' faintin', an' Marie, she held on to the seat to stop from swoonin'.

"Keepers ran up, guns in hand, but the captain, he told 'em not to shoot. He walked slowly an' quietly out o' that cage just as if he were walkin' behind a weddin'. People cheered an' cried, but Marie quickly tied his hand, pulled him out, an' put him in a carriage to rush him to the doctor.

"She held his arm lovingly, an' then she saw for the first time that Captain Bonavita's black curly locks . . . were gone! They were only a wig coverin' his bald head!

"Well, glory be! D'ye think that made a difference to that lovin' lass? No difference at all. Captain Bonavita related how he lost his own black curly locks battlin' with wild lions an' tigers who tore the flesh from his body an' the hair from his head.

"That made Marie love her brave captain even more than she had loved him before, which is the right an' proper thing for a woman to do."

Mike was silent. The men lying around in the sun laughed, and Mike was pleased as any fine storyteller would be.

That's the kind of stories you'll hear when you're up in Stauch's Solarium, where men lie around like red lizards, waiting to take their dip in the surf in Coney Island by the Sea.

A Baker's Dozen

UP IN Albany, the capital of New York State, the Empire State, there's a story folks have been telling for near two hundred years, and it is so good a story it'll be told for all the years to come, and maybe after then.

Now I will tell you that story, the like of which there is no better. For folks in New York State say all things there are bigger and better than in all the U.S.A., and I am not one to deny it.

In the simple old days there lived in Albany, or Beverwyck, as it was known then, a baker with many Dutch names, one of which was Jan, and Jan I'll call him.

Jan was famous up the Hudson and down the Hudson and all around the Hudson land for baking the finest gingerbread New Year's cookies. They were shaped like fat little angels and like the good Saint Nicholas, the holy saint of all the Dutch burghers.

One clear cold day before the New Year he sat in his shop, full of joy at the sunny world around him, when there was a sharp knock at his door.

It opened before he could open his mouth, and there stood an old lady with a beaked nose and burning eyes.

"Baas Volckert Jan Pietersen Van Amsterdam," she cried shrilly, "sell me a good dozen of your finest New Year cookies and be quick about it. I must go on a long journey before the New Year is out."

"You don't have to scream so loud, good dame," Jan mumbled as he counted out six fat, lovely, brown ginger-bread babies and six fat Saint Nicholas cakes with miters and sugared crooks. He gave them to her, and she counted them.

"A dozen I said," she screamed. "A dozen!" And she brought down her cane with a fierce thump on the wooden floor. "This is not a dozen. There's only twelve. Count 'em."

"I don't have to count 'em. Since when is twelve NOT a dozen?"

Jan really couldn't understand the queer old lady.

Again she began screaming and thumping her cane. "Twelve is not a dozen. One more is a dozen. Twelve is not a dozen."

"Now, let me tell you, old lady, twelve is a dozen in my shop the same as in all of Beverwyck and all New Amsterdam, too, and in old Amsterdam as well, for that matter."

"I want a dozen," she screamed again. "My kind of dozen."

"In my baker shop you buy my kind of dozen. And if you don't like it take yourself elsewhere—even to the Devil, and quickly, to boot."

"I'll teach you a lesson for this," the old dame shouted

as she flung out of the shop, thumping her cane and leaving the door wide open for the cold to come in.

"Good riddance," Jan said angrily while he closed the door with a bang.

His wife came in to see what the rumpus was about.

Now, Jan's wife was well-favored and wise, and when she heard the tale she said:

"Perhaps, good Jan, you should have given the poor old woman the extra cookie as a New Year's gift. 'Twouldn't have made you a poor man."

"I'm glad I didn't," Jan replied angrily. But that was only the beginning of his anger.

From the very next day things began to go wrong with Baas Volckert Jan Pietersen Van Amsterdam.

His breads burned in the oven or turned sour. Sometimes they became strangely light as a feather and sometimes heavy as stone. At times they even vanished in the air.

Folks didn't come to his shop as often, bricks flew into his windows thrown by unseen hands, and chunks of wood from his wood pile flew at his head when he walked to the shed. Poor Jan did not know what to do or where to turn.

One late afternoon he was sitting in his shop, full of misery, when there was a sharp knock at the door. It opened at once, and who should it be but the little old woman with the hooked nose, sharp eyes, and the yellow wrinkled face.

"Will you now sell me a proper dozen of cookies?" she screamed.

That was more than Jan could bear. "No, I'll not," he roared. "You old witch, get out of my sight! Get out and get out quick."

He rushed to the door, but it closed in his face. A cackling laughter was heard outside which made him even more angry.

Time went on, and things went worse with Jan. Now his good wife was becoming deaf and could hardly help him any more.

He sat in his shop, his heart full of bitterness, when there was again a sharp knock at the door. It opened a little, and the same old woman just stuck in her nose and dark eyes and opened her mouth wide, screaming:

"Will you now sell me the right kind of dozen—twelve and one?"

"Not I, you old witch," shouted Jan. He leaped up and ran to the door, but it was closed. He opened it, but no one was in sight.

His children took ill, as if poor Jan did not have enough miseries. He truly believed that Job in the Bible did not have as many troubles as were his.

It was near Christmas season in Beverwyck once again, and poor Jan was sitting in his shop, his head bowed low in anger and disappointment, when there was a knock at the door. It opened only a little space, and a sharp nose came in with a shrill voice screaming:

"How much is a dozen? Twelve, or twelve and one?"

Before he could reach the door it was closed, and Jan walked back to his seat slowly.

"Oh, Good Lord and good Saint Nicholas! No matter what I do, all goes wrong. Won't you come to my aid!"

No sooner were the words out of his mouth than there was a shadow across the window and there was a slow knocking at the door. The door opened, and there stood Saint Nicholas dressed in gold and scarlet lace, and behind him was a fine white steed with jingle bells and silver saddle.

His face was sweet and kind and smiling.

"I'll gladly help you, good Jan. You have always made fine images of me, which young and old love dearly. You are a kind man, but you lose your temper quickly. That is a failing with many people."

"Maybe I do, maybe I do," Jan mumbled, for he knew the good saint told the very truth.

"Now," said the saint, "I know your troubles well. You must not lose your temper and must be kind to old women, as you are generous to children. Remember kindness grows broad trees. When that old woman comes again for a dozen cookies, you give her just what she wants: twelve and one more for good measure. We'll call that a good baker's dozen. If you'll do what I say, all your troubles will end. Now, Jan, I must go elsewhere, for I am a very busy saint this time of the year. A happy day to you and a good year to you."

Jan thanked the good Saint Nicholas over and over

again and led him to the door. The saint mounted his fine white horse and rode off with jingling bells.

No sooner was he gone and the door was closed than there was again a sharp knocking. The door opened, and there stood the same little old woman with the sharp nose and the wrinkled face.

"I want a dozen cookies," she said shrilly.

"And a dozen cookies you shall have, old lady. A baker's dozen fit for the Christmas holiday and fit for the New Year."

A dozen she got, and one more besides, and from that day on Baas Volckert Jan Pietersen Van Amsterdam of Beverwyck's troubles were at an end.

His cookies became famous once again up the Hudson, down the Hudson, all around the Hudson land. His wife could hear, and his children were well.

Since that time a baker's dozen in New York State is not just twelve like in any other state, but twelve and one.

Which is as it should be. For isn't New York State the Empire State of the U.S.A., where things are bigger and better than in any other state, as folks of New York always say—and who am I to tell them otherwise?

Pig in the Poke

IN Oneida County, where the Mohawk River and the Erie Canal circle around, there are enough tales about smart folks to fill the Good Book. And the smartest tales are told about General William Floyd. He was a hero, a statesman, and a man who loved a joke as much as a good gun. Folks tell stories about him that'd take months to tell, and here is one to whet your appetite for more.

The general had many men working for him, and there was one among them called Long John, who was the best fox-hunting man in all the town. His cabin was just full of foxes' skins and foxes' tails, and he was mighty proud of 'em.

One fall of the year, when the general was butchering hogs, the largest, fattest one was full of measles and couldn't be eaten at all.

Said the general to Long John:

"John, you can have that pig, meat and all. Use it for bait for the foxes, for it can't be eaten nohow."

John thanked the general, but when the sun had set and the stars were out he loaded the dead pig to be used for fox bait in a wheelbarrow, took it to a store man who wasn't too honest in his weights, and offered it for sale.

They higgled and they haggled, for John would only take the top o' the market price and the store man offered less than half. In the end the price was set.

The store man bought the porker, thinking he had stolen the pig and got a goose in his sleeve besides. But John went with the money, laughing to himself, thinking, you believe you're mighty smart, Mister Store Man, but this time you bought a pig in a poke.

The next morning, when the sun shone crisp, the store man looked at the hog and saw it was full of measles and couldn't be sold to folks unless he'd want the law on his head. **694524**

He ran to General Floyd, crying and shouting he had been cheated by the general's man and with the general's pig.

The general called Long John, and John came, grinning all over his wrinkled face.

"John, I gave you that pig to use for fox bait because I told you it was sick and could not be et. You went and sold it to the store man. That's cheating."

"I didn't do no cheatin', Massa," said John.

The general saw he'd have to make it clearer.

"John, what did I tell you to do with that hog?" the general said with a stern face.

"Massa General, you tole me to use the measly pig for baitin' foxes."

"And what did you do with it?"

"Massa General, I caught the biggest fox in town with it."

Now, there was a smart answer Solomon the wise couldn't say better.

The general laughed his fill, and even the store man had to join in it.

Said the general:

"John, a good laugh is worth more than money in this world o' troubles."

He opened his wallet, took out some money, and, turning to the store man, added:

"Here, take the money you paid John for the measly pig. John can keep what you paid him for his wits."

So both were satisfied, and the general was satisfied, too. And all the folks of Oneida County were also satisfied, for wherever they heard the story up and down and all around the county they joined in the laughter.

Adirondack Skeeters

THE mosquitoes in our land are the best and biggest mosquitoes in all the world. And the biggest an' best of these are right in our own New York State, and don't let any man contradict you.

Right at the beginnin', when Hudson sailed up the river, these skeeters were man-eatin' 'nuf to swallow Indians for breakfast an' pick their teeth with the ribs.

It got so bad the Indians prayed to their god t' come and help 'em. There was a fierce battle at salt Lake Onondaga 'bout which Indian warriors sing to this day.

The great skeeters were killed, but their blood soaked in the earth, and up came new skeeters smaller but more pesky than the old. They didn't kill, they stung!

They stung deepest of all in the Adirondack Mountains in New York State. That's the mountains where you find the Walloper critter that's got one pair o' legs shorter than t'other so it kin climb easy, and the Wooly Nig that's got five legs and two tails—but the skeeters were worst of all.

The lumbermen couldn't stand 'em, and the lumber foreman tried his best to rid his camp of those skeeters that never stopped stingin' the crews.

Now, up around Mt. Marcy around Blue Mountain Lake a crew of lumbermen were cuttin' trees fast 'nuf to please Paul Bunyan. They were cuttin' hemlock an' pine in the daytime an' singin' in the nighttime "The Jam at Gerry's Rock," "Blue Mountain Lake" and other songs, and tellin' tales about Bunyan and Greenfield.

Everything would have been smooth 's butter if not for them pesky skeeters. Sufferin' cats! Nothin' could stop 'em. Neither gun nor fire nor smoke. Worst of all, them bitin' bugs were thick 's pea soup.

Lumbermen had to work in woolen shirts though the sun was hot, an' in high boots though there weren't no mud. Every night when they were tryin' to sing or tell tales the skeeters'd make 'em crawl under hot sheets.

It was gettin' worse all the time. One day the men came to the foreman and said they would not do another split o' work if he didn't do somethin' about it.

The foreman scratched his head and scratched his back and said he'd think on it.

He thought all day when the axes were choppin' an' the skeeters were zoomin', an' he thought all night when the bugs were makin' noises louder than the bullfrogs in the ponds. Just when the cock was crowin' he had a fine idea.

"We can't kill them skeeters, there is too many of 'em. But here is somethin' might do it. Let's get bumblebees from the valley. Bumblebees has stingers in front, skeeters has 'em in the back. Bumblebees'll see that an' think skeeters are foreign critters tryin' to steal their lands an' surely will drive 'em off."

Foreman and crew, they went down the valleys and got bumblebees in boxes an' bags. They fed 'em on sugar an' honey to make 'em good an' strong.

Singin' "Turkey in the Straw," they brought 'em to camp and let the bumblebees loose to battle the skeeters. Then the men went to sleep, figurin' 'twas the end of the skeeters.

The bumblebees, they met the skeeters an' saw no reason for battlin'. They said "How d'y do," friendly like, an' went courtin' instead.

An' when they were married, came children that were even worse than the old Adirondack skeeters. The new generation of skeeters, they had stingers in front and in back as well!

That's how come Adirondack skeeters in New York State are unlike any skeeters in the land. But then, y' know, most critters up in them mountains around the many lakes are different from any critters in the land. If y' don't believe me go and see for yourself.

> Open your ears and open your eyes,
> Am tellin' the truth, can't tell no lies.

Sam Patch,
the Jumpin' Man

SAM PATCH the jumpin' man was a jumpin' man from his cradle days.

One day his granny held him lovingly in her arms as his mother was kneeling over the washtub full of clothes and water. Kerplunk! that boy, he jumped right down into the tubful o' wash and was pulled out full o' suds.

"That bub's the smartest baby in creation," old Granny said.

"It's a good thing he didn't break his neck," his mother said.

When he was still an itsy bit of a feller and crawled around on hands and feet, he jumped with the jumping frogs and jumped with the crickets.

And his dad said: "That boy's jumpin' more than's good for a boy. Y' know what folks say? Quicker he learns to use his head, quicker his heels'll be safe."

When he got to school he jumped from the desk and he jumped from the benches, he jumped from the trees and he jumped from the roof. He also jumped over spelling hard words and jumped over classes he didn't like, but that wasn't so good.

"Sam, y'll jump once too often, and it'll be worse than jumpin' from the fryin' pan into the fire," the teacher said. "Remember y're a growin' boy, and plantin' rocks means reapin' tears."

But Sam, he was a frisky young fellow who didn't listen to what old heads said. His granny, she said: "He was just feelin' his wings."

One fine day Daddy Patch took young Sammy Patch in a rollicking boat on a trip around New York, and they got as far as roaring Hell Gate.

Sammy took a look at the seething water and shouted out loud:

"I like it good an' hot," and jumped right into the jumpin' waves.

Father and captain fished him out with a ten-foot pole and dried him in the wind and sun.

"Watch out for that jumpin' lad," the captain said to Father Patch. "Teach him the difference atween careful an' careless, lest he come to a weepin' end."

"I'm doin' the best I can," Father Patch replied. "That boy seems to favor jumpin' more than anythin' else. I hope he don't jump too much one day."

When Sam was a young man he went to work in a cotton mill, and do you think he tended his spindles and spinning like the others did? Not he. He even kept the others from workin' by jumping from the peaked roof of the mill into the quiet water below, or from the bridge that was over it. He did this near every day and most often on Sunday.

The minister wanted the people to be in church on Sunday, or at home thinking of heavenly things.

"People should stay home on Sunday and say their prayers," he said. "One day Sam Patch, he'll jump too much and land where he hadn't ought ter."

But you might 's well talk to the deaf and dumb.

One day Sam picked himself up and went to New Jersey. He came to Paterson and walked as far as the Passaic Falls that rush down the dizzy heights with a deafening noise.

Workmen were busy building a bridge over the deep chasm to make walking easier, and many a walker and many a driver passing by stopped to watch the working folks work.

"If many folks watch bridge-makers makin' a bridge, many more are likely to watch a jumper jump from a high cliff into the churnin' water," Sam Patch said to himself.

So, on the day when they were ready to swing the bridge across, and there was the greatest crowd, Sam Patch said he'd jump the falls.

Policemen and citizens tried to stop him, but who could stop Sam Patch the Jumpin' Man from jumpin' when he made up his mind to jump?

He got on high when no one was looking.

The falls were roaring, a great crowd was watching the score of muscled men setting the bridge across, when, kersmack!, one of the rolling pins with the guide rope fell from off the swinging bridge down seventy feet into the deep water. There was shouting and crying, but there was even louder shouting and crying, near loud as the roaring falls, when folks spied Sam Patch standing on high where the pine and hemlocks grew.

Then—the crowd looked on with frightened and staring eyes. Sam took a jump! A jump full seventy feet down, deep, deep into the water—came up—got hold of pin and rope, came through the water with 'em to those who'd have stopped him from jumping down.

Cried he, "Now you see that some things can be done as well as others."

The crowd roared wild acclaim, but a wise man, an officer of the law, said:

"Sam Patch, this time ye got away, they always do the first time, but then comes the second time, or maybe the third. We al'ays catch 'm in the end. And maybe one day you'll be caught. It's better to stop early than to be caught late."

Do you think Sam Patch the Jumpin' Man heard the good policeman's warning? Not by old Jehoshaphat.

"It's only the beginning," he cried. "I'm a great hero, an' I kin do anythin' better'n others."

So he moved nearer New York State, the Empire State, which was just the right place for such a great man.

One fine day, when the sun shone bright on the dancing water of the Hudson River and all New Yorkers from New York City and Jerseyites from across were watching, Sam got on a boat, climbed on the masthead to jump from the top, full ninety feet high. He was jumping higher and higher all the time.

When Manhattanites and Jerseyites and "ites" of other states saw that great jump of Sam Patch the Jumpin' Man they thought they'd like to try some jumping, too. Newsboys jumped from off steps and railings, clerks jumped from off the counters. Girls jumped from off the benches, and Bowery b'hoys jumped from off the lampposts. Farmers jumped from off the hayloads, and young boys jumped from off the roofs. So all the country was jumping jumps just like Sam Patch the Jumpin' Man.

Sam was proud, Sam was rambumptious, he said he was the almightiest man alive, and he'd show it to all the world. He would take the biggest jump any man ever took; he'd jump down Niagara Falls! The mightiest, the riproarinest, the thunderationest falls in all the world.

Preachers preached against it, said it was tempting the Lord and that pride goeth before a fall. Wise men shook their heads, raised their eyebrows, and said the angel became a Devil when he fell too far. All the land was scared, all the people agin it.

Sam Patch shook his head and cried:

"Napoleon is conquerin' the world, but I've conquered jumpin' from high places. Watch me!"

They built a ladder of four giant trees and, on the top, a little platform just enough for a man to stand on. Below was the roaring, raging, angry, foaming Niagara Falls.

Sam Patch stood high up on the little stand while a

great crowd thick as flies on honey bread stood below.

He took off his shoes and took off his coat, he took his kerchief from his neck and tied it around his waist. He waved his hand to the thousands standing on the American shores, and on the Canadian side as well. Then he kissed the American flag and . . . jumped clear through the air! . . .

Women screamed and shut their eyes, children lay down on the ground; men held their breath, and young ones heard their hearts thumping!

Bang! There was a high, pearly splash when Sam hit the water, and all looked eagerly and breathlessly to see!

A minute! Sam Patch the Jumpin' Man came up from the water fresh as a trout and just as wet.

The crowd roared, the crowd cheered! Some cried, some laughed. The air was full of hurrahing and whistling and screaming, all for Sam Patch the Jumpin' Man, the greatest man in the U.S.A.

It made Sam proud as a peacock. He thought he was greater than Davy Crockett and, like that hero, got him a bear for a pet who walked with him wherever he went.

One day he came to Genesee Falls, his friend the bear by his side, for the greatest jump of all.

His name was in all the papers, and they said a great many things. They said, "Sam Patch Against the World."

"HIGHER YET. SAM'S LAST JUMP. SOME THINGS CAN BE DONE AS WELL AS OTHERS. THERE IS NO MISTAKE IN SAM PATCH," read the posters.

Preachers cried Sam was tempting God. Goodmen

cried it was gambling with the Lord. Bluenoses said it was a shame to see a man tempt heaven, but, just the same, folks came by the thousands. They came by boat and they came on foot; they came by coach and on horse. They came from every county and every state to see Sam take his great jump.

The day was warm, and the crowd was so thick you could not move. On the banks, on the roofs, on horses, on carriages, wherever the eye could see, it was thick with eager faces.

Soon Sam Patch was standing on high on the platform, a kerchief around his neck, while his bear stood below, waiting to jump.

Sam took his kerchief from off his neck and tied it around his waist. He waved to the crowd and made 'em a speech. He waved his hand to the right and left, and the crowd held its breath.

Then he jumped! . . .

The water closed over him, the spray splashed high! Then a minute! Another!! Another!!! But no Sam Patch coming up! . . .

Men shouted, women screamed, young 'uns cried.

Some leaped in boats, some leaped in the water, others began dragging with hooks and grapples!

But there was no Sam Patch. Folks said Sam Patch was dead.

Preachers said Sam had tempted the Lord once too often; goodmen cried Sam Patch gambled once too high, bluenoses growled he got his just reward.

But bluenoses, preachers, and goodmen were wrong. Heroes just don't die like that.

Sam Patch the Jumpin' Man fell deep, deep in the water and thought it'd be fine for a great hero to see a little of the rest of the world. He swam and swam and swam till he came out in the China Sea, where a New England sea captain who never told a lie said he saw him. He said Sam Patch was doing marvelous American deeds out there in the heathen lands.

And, for all I know, Sam may still be around some place, jumping from heights no man had ever jumped from before.

Maiden Lane
in the Golden Days

HERE'S a day in the golden days of Maiden Lane in New York City, when New York the Great was New York the Little.

There was a ghost in Maiden Lane, a tall, white ghost that walked with heavy slow steps along the curving street from Broadway to the Fly Market on the East River. Each night that ghost walked in the white moonlight dressed in a long, flowing, white mantle, screaming and screeching and frightening goodmen and goodwives on their homeward way from neighbors and from inns.

For a long time that ghost scared young and old, until one day a doughty captain of a clipper said:

"I'm not afraid of ghosts on the sea when ships are torn in twain by wild and roaring winds, and of a surety I'm not afraid of a landlubber ghost scaring folks on Maiden Lane. I'll tackle that ghost in a good old-fashioned seafaring way."

When the sun went down and the moon came up over little New York City, over Maiden Lane, over the East

River, the fearless captain began walking up and down the rounding street.

He walked slowly from broad Broadway to the Fly Market on the River, up and back, while the watchman, lantern in hand, made his nightly rounds crying, "All's well." So it came to midnight.

The captain in his brown greatcoat was still pacing the streets with rolling steps when suddenly he heard screaming and yelling like wild Indians on the warpath, but he did not run as all others had. He stood his ground, and there was the tall, white ghost coming toward him.

When the ghost was close upon him, the courageous captain drew forth a fat, wooden cudgel cut from a hickory tree and began belaboring that ghost with might and main.

The ghost fell down, the white mantle fell off, and there was a cry for mercy.

And what do you think that ghost on Maiden Lane was? Only a wag of the town, a crafty fellow who thought he'd have some fun with the good folks of Maiden Lane.

The ghost cried, "Ha' mercy," and the captain cried, "B' gad, I'll forgive ye," and they went into the inn and drank a tankard of ale.

The next morning all the town was agog with the happenings of the night. It was market day, when all the farmers came with their greens, butter and eggs, and fruits to the Fly Market to sell and barter. Merchant men were there, shoemakers, jewelers, hoopmakers, and the noise they made blabbering was greater than that made by the little river winding through Maiden Lane and running into the wide East River.

They didn't speak of the new playhouse or the doings of the young men at the new Columbia College. They only spoke of the sham ghost and the brave captain. And when the captain came walking along with a Quaker friend, all greeted them with good cheer.

All save old Hans, who sat on his three-legged stool selling the finest butter in the market wrapped with the greatest care. Hans was a surly man, and 'twas often whispered that his butter was short of weight.

Of a sudden his face grew wan and worried, for there was the weightmaster coming down the road to find if any merchant was cheating in his weights or measures. Someone had whispered to the weightmaster to watch Hans the butter man, who was not giving full weight on his pound rolls of yellow butter.

But Hans was sly even as he was surly. No sooner did he see the weightmaster in his three-cornered hat than he quickly slipped a guinea piece between the top roll of yellow butter and its cover, so that it would have the full and proper weight the law demanded. For, as usual, he had shortweighted his butter. But Man tries and God decrees.

It so happened that the Quaker walking with the captain had stopped and listened and had seen how the old rogue tried to hoodwink the weightmaster by slipping in the guinea piece to give the first roll of butter full weight. The officer came up to the butter man.

"Good morrow," said he.

"Good morrow," Hans replied. "I wot you're looking for those who cheat the people of our town."

"That I am indeed," said the weightmaster. "I've heard said that your rolls of butter fall short of their desired weight."

"Saints forbid! Here, Master! Here, pick the roll of butter lying here and weigh it."

He took the roll of butter lying on the top that had the guinea piece hidden in it and gave it to the weightmaster.

The officer opened his black box with the scales and put the butter on it. It weighed a full pound—even a little more than the law required.

The weightmaster thought that he had been misinformed and that Hans was an honest man.

By then a great crowd had gathered around the butter man and the weightmaster. Said the Quaker who was with the captain to old Hans:

"Master Hans, since you sell butter of honest weight, I'll buy a pound roll of it."

And before Hans could even answer him, he took the top roll of butter, the one that had the guinea piece in it.

Hans reached out quickly for the roll and cried with beating heart:

"Nay, not this one, Friend. I've sold this to a friend of mine. Take the next. It's just as good."

"Nay, I want this one," the Quaker said.

"Ye can't have it, I told ye I sold it."

"The buyer has the right to choose the merchandise he wants if he's willing to pay for it," the captain said. "Give your friend another roll, since they are all alike."

"But I want him to have this one," Hans cried with perspiration on his forehead.

"I appeal to thee, good weightmaster," said the Quaker, turning to him. "Have I not the right to choose the merchandise for which I am willing to pay good money, just as my friend the captain said?"

"You have that right, Master Quaker and Master Captain. As for you, Master Hans, if all the rolls of butter are alike, what matter which you give your friend?"

What could Hans say? What could he do? He couldn't even show anger on his face.

The smiling Quaker kept the roll of butter with the guinea and gave dishonest Hans three shillings for the butter.

Said he with a pleasant smile on his broad face:

"Friend, thee and I know full well cheating is not a profitable game, that's why I know thee are no cheat," and the Quaker went away together with the captain.

"You caught the rogue in his snare," the captain said with a smile.

"The same as you caught the ghost rogue yesterday," the Quaker quickly replied. "Knaves' pleasures often end in pain."

Such are the tales told of the Golden Days in Maiden Lane in New York City.

Canawlers on
the E-ri-ee Canal

IN THE jolly fighting days of the E-ri-ee Canal, the boats went upstate as far as Buffalo and downstate as far as New York, and, oh! there was fun, fight, frolic, and pleasure for passengers and for crews.

Those were crews! They loved fighting more than boating up and down Clinton Ditch, as the canal was often called, and many a one was famous for his fists.

There was Sleepy Frank, and the Black Bully who could leap clear across the widest part of the canal, and there was the Rochester Bully who fought the Bully of Buffalo and every other bully that worked on the muddy waters.

And while the patient horses were pulling the heavy, loaded boats with the round bows and square sterns, there were great shoutings at the locks. The "Canawlers" roared:

> "I've got a mule, her name is Sal,
> Fifteen miles on the E-ri-ee Canal."

and they sang "Paddy on the Canal" and other songs. They also fought battles and talked tall talk.

One time there was a long wait around the village of Cuba, where they built a large lake to feed the canal with water when it ran low and dry. There was a bad break on the locks further down that stopped the boats from moving. All were laid up—"wild boats," which were boats from other canals, and regular E-ri-ee boats. They lay bow to stern so you could walk from one to another as on a bridge.

The crews sat around with nothing to do but talk and argue and have a little fun, but some of the men, they went on shore to Cuba to visit the groceries and the stores.

That's just what the crew of the *Diantha Mariah* was doing. One of the men stayed behind, but the captain and the rest of the crew went ashore.

Soon they met some fast boys of the town, bullies who never let good citizens be at peace or canal-boat crews mind their own business.

These fast boys of the town called the crews that didn't fight petticoat pirates and other such names. They pushed 'em around and treated 'em rough, they pulled off their hats and tore their coats. And the men of the *Diantha Mariah* watched them at their game.

Said Slim, the bowman of the boat:

"I'd give me best boots to put these fellows in their place."

"And I'd do the same, by holy Saint Patrick," added Hank, the steersman.

"Tell ye what," said Captain Dirk, who knew the ways of life and was a pretty slick man, "ye make friends with these bullies while I go back on the boat. Tell 'em there's plenty o' vittles on the *Diantha Mariah* an' plenty o' drink, an' in my cabin there's a load o' monkeys from Afriky I am carryin' for the circus in Buffalo. Tell 'em t' come aboard an' eat an' drink an' make merry with the monkeys. In the meanwhile I'll get the crew from the *Mayfly* an' maybe the *Star* an' hide 'em down below. Then when ye got 'em aboard with promises, an' the plank is off from the shore, I'll come out with me men an' we'll teach these fast boys a lesson they'll remember for time t' come. I'm pretty sure they'll not be botherin' peaceful citizens or canawlers at their work after that."

The captain and two of the men returned while Slim and Hank remained.

It didn't take long before they were friends with the town's fast boys in their high-colored shirts and high boots. Soon they were begging to go to the *Diantha Mariah* to eat the food and drink the drinks and play with the monkeys from Africa.

Slim led them to the canal, where the horses were grazing quietly, and then on the boat. When they were all aboard Slim pulled in the running plank.

The town fast boys began stomping about, crying for food and drink and monkeys, when suddenly from the cabin came captain and crews from the *Mayfly* and from the *Star* as well.

They leaped on the fast boys and laid them low. Hair

was flying and strong words, too. Now and then there was a big splash that meant another fast boy cooling off in the water. There'd be a spluttering and splashing in the shallow canal, and words that made the yellow moon hide in shame behind the clouds.

In the end there was a gay crowd of canawlers on the *Diantha Mariah* and wiser heads among the fast boys of the town.

When the next Canal boat put in at Cuba village, the fast boys of the town thought twice or maybe three times before making sport of the crews or law-abiding citizens, and you know why.

Lady Morris
in Her Mansion

IN THE days that are gone, Gouverneur Morris was a noted statesman in our land, a minister to royal France. He built a great mansion and filled it with all the rich treasures gotten from noble French refugees when they fled from the bloody revolution.

The riches were so vast that his nearest of kin looked on them with greedy eyes, hoping for the statesman's death to get them.

But it was to be otherwise.

One day, when Minister Morris and his wife and kinsmen were sitting at a grand feast, he raised his glass on high and cried a toast to his wife and the hope that she might bear him a son to inherit his great fortune.

The kinsmen who sat at the table were silent, with black looks on their faces. But man desires and God decrees, and one year later Anne Morris bore a son to her good husband. But by this time the minister, alas, was no more! He had gone to join his forefathers.

All the kinfolks swore that Anne Morris and her son

would never get the riches—they would find means to stop them.

New Year's eve came, and Mistress Anne was sitting in a high chamber in her mansion before the blazing fire, her young son in her arms. She let the servants go for the evening, mourning in silence the loss of her husband.

Of a sudden there was a sound of hoofbeats on the road, and soon a gruff voice shouted at the door:

"Open the door, Anne Morris, and bring out your husband's will, else it will fare ill with you and your son."

Anne stood still in white fright, and her heart near stopped beating. She held her son tight in her arms.

Again there was a hard pounding at the door:

"Open the door, woman, and bring out what I tell you, or we'll break the door down and get it."

Poor Mistress Anne, she could not move. What should she do? There were surely a few men out there, hard and pitiless, and she was alone and helpless.

Suddenly there was a rustling behind her. She turned her head, and a sight greeted her that froze her even more and made her speechless!

She couldn't trust her eyes! The figure in the painting of one of the Morris's great ancestors, a man with sword and mail, had come to life! The old warrior stepped out of the picture frame and cried out aloud:

"Gouverneur Morris! Come forth! Your wife and heir are in peril and need your aid."

There was a sound of moving steps from the bed-chamber where Gouverneur Morris had died and where his own portrait hung. The door opened wide, and there he stood in person, dressed the same as in his portrait.

The two ghostly men walked to the door and opened it wide.

Three men standing there, ready to rush in, stopped, nailed to the ground.

"For shame, you ruffians and thieves! I'm ashamed to call ye kinsmen," Gouverneur Morris cried. "You come to attack a helpless woman and rob an innocent child. You are not worth the name of men, let alone kinfolk. Go your way quickly and never come near my house, or you'll rue the day you ever had an evil thought."

The three men fled to their horses and rode off swifter than arrows from a bow.

Gouverneur Morris closed the door and led his wife and the child in her arms through the chambers, showing her all the wealth. Then he and the armored man were gone as if in a dream. . . .

The portraits in their gilded frames were exactly as before.

Mistress Anne was bewildered, but she knew it was no dream, for neither kith nor kin ever bothered her again; they let her and her son live in peace with all their rich belongings.

A New Way
of Tamin' Wolves

FOLKS tell plenty o' tales about Saratoga city up New York State. They tell about the healin' springs where old people turn young, an' they tell about swell folks dressed in fancy clothes, an' women in peacock feathers with diamonds all over, an' gamblers bettin' millions on a horse. But I'm goin' to tell you about the plain folks in Saratoga Springs, those who roamed in the woods an' fished in the lakes, not those who lived in the high-class hotels an' followed the races.

In those fine old days there lived Pete, a fishin' an' huntin' man. He was also as fine a cook as ever cooked in a great hotel in Saratoga Springs.

For that reason great folks, judges, and senators came to his little shack on Saratoga Lake to eat the finest bass ever broiled on fire an' t' go fishin' with him.

When fishin' was poor, Pete 'd tell about his adventures that are told to this very day, when such adventures are no more.

The story he liked best to tell an' told most often is

60

the story of how he conquered a pack o' wolves with his fiddlin'.

Now, Pete, he fished an' cooked, but what he liked just as much as fishin' an' cookin' was fiddlin' at frolics an' weddin's.

One late night, maybe it was early in the morning, Pete was comin' home from a frolic where he had been fiddlin' the whole night long. His violin was tight under his arm, his pelt cap over his ears, his hands deep in his pockets, for it was bitter cold. Only the stars on high still shinin' clear and a silver moon runnin' wild through the black clouds weren't cold that night.

Pete was comin' near his neck o' the woods when he heard a howlin' he didn't like. It was black wolves, more fierce than any wildcat in the woods.

Pete didn't carry a gun with him. He figured he was too near home an' no beast 'd bother him.

Well, here was a whole pack o' black wolves, tongues hangin' out, eyes red like fire, hungry 'nuf to eat bark.

Now, Pete was a quick-thinkin' man, an' he remembered there was an old log house right nearby, broken down an' deserted, where he might find shelter against the wild beasts.

He ran quick 's his legs 'd go an' came to the place just when the wolves were near snappin' his heels. He ran inside it, but the door wouldn't close. Quick 's a flash he climbed up a big beam in the middle.

I must tell you Pete was long an' bony, and it wasn't an easy matter for him to sit on the wooden beam.

The wolves came in, six of 'em, an' seein' Pete on high set up a fierce howlin' like a pack of Indians out for a scalpin' party. 'Twasn't no pleasure straddlin' on that beam, listenin' to the beasts yelpin' an' yowlin', leapin' higher an' higher in the dark, gleamin' eyes an' hot stinkin' breath comin' up.

Pete listened to that night music for a spell, while sittin' on the beam was gettin' harder all the time. His legs began achin', but he was afraid of hangin' 'em down lest the yelpin' beasts snap 'm an' pull 'm down.

Then Pete had a queer thought in his mind for no reason at all. He said to himself aloud:

"If I kin make folks dance to the tunes of my fiddle mebe I kin stop that pernickity yelpin' that's near tearin' my ears t' pieces, an' mebe I kin stretch my legs down for a spell."

So he took his fiddle and raised his bow and began fiddlin' tunes. First 'twas "Yankee Doodle," then "Turkey in the Straw." Next 'twas "Old Joe Clark," and then every other reel, song, an' dance that came to his mind.

Prancin' horses! With the first tune the beasts stopped their howlin' an' just looked at him. With the next they sat down, lookin' more at Fiddlin' Pete. With the third he slid his legs down slowly, an' the wolves sat still an' never bothered him.

Then somethin' happened Pete did not like. Maybe 'twas the cold, maybe a string was too tight, but right in the middle of a song one o' them strings bust in two. Pete stopped his playin'. But no sooner did he stop than the wolves began their howlin' wildly all over again.

So once again Pete began fiddlin' with his freezin' hands on the freezin' cold fiddle. He was an old hand at playin' tunes an' could play on three strings just as well as on four.

Soon again, maybe it was the cold in the fiddle, maybe the cold in his hands, another string bust in two.

Pete kept on fiddlin' on two strings. The music wasn't good 'nuf for dancin' partners but 'twas good enough for yelpin' wolves.

But luck wasn't with 'm. Soon the third string bust, an' there was just one string left.

Pete, he kept on playin' on one single string, but it was sorrowful tunes he played, bad 'nuf to make cats yowl.

B'lieve it or not, but I'll say it on the Holy Book, them wolves didn't favor the playin' on a single string.

Once again they set up a fierce yowlin' an' yelpin' an' began leapin'. Pete had to draw up his legs quick, else he'd have no legs at all.

Seemed the beasts now leaped higher an' fiercer than before, an' they was comin' mighty near Pete's boots an' pants. It looked as if Pete had done his last fiddlin'. But ye know, "when the thunder's longest a rainbow's nearest."

The stars had gone from the sky, an' there were streaks of mornin' in the east. Folks were comin' on the road, some neighbors with a team of oxen goin' for logs. They heard the howlin' an' quickly saved Pete the fiddler's head from blossomin' in a wintry grave.

From then on, Fiddlin' Pete never went fiddlin' without carryin' extra strings for his fiddle.

The Witch Tree
of the North Country

IN THE North Country of New York State, where Fenimore Cooper wrote his Indian tales, there are many more stories that remain to be told. I heard some on warm summer days when I came to listen to other storytellers up there near Lake Otesago.

In the fine, white house by the wayside where I stayed lived a thin little woman with graying hair and a round stout man with a ruddy face.

In the gay summer months they sold gasoline, and in the cold wintertime they went to "Floridee" to fill themselves with the sun and the salty sea. Said they, "It's the best doctorin' there is for aches an' miseries." And when we sat evenings on the wide, white porch they told me stories folks tell around those parts.

"There lived a man up there, in the days of the big bloody war of brother against brother, who was a mighty mean creature. He wasn't scared of God or Devil. The only thing that ever worried him was gittin' more money all the time. The more he had, the more he wanted. Well, you know thems that wants too much ends poor before their time's up.

"In those days the gov'ment was buyin' silver money, only cows know why, so this mean man, he got to buyin' all the silver from neighbors and travelin' folks and hid it away so's to sell it to the gov'ment in Washington.

"Now, you know a man 'can't hide for long in a hollow tree,' and soon near everybody around Cooperstown, far as Richfield Springs down to Oneonte, knew all about this hoardin' of silver.

"One gray day, when that man, greedy as a dog, had nosed around buyin' more silver and was on his way home, some fellows worse'n himself waylaid him in the woods. They took from him the silver in his belt and made 'm tell where the rest was hidden in his house and barn. Then they went and killed him, choppin' off his head, and threw him into the bushes.

"They went to his house, got the rest of the hoarded silver, and began thinkin' what to do.

"You know the old saw, 'a guilty conscience 's scared of itself.'

"The robbers thought the law was after 'em already, and so they buried the silver, figurin' t' get it when the tale had blown over. But man, he plows, and rain and sun do as they please.

"The murderers forgot the spot where they buried the silver!

"Folks found the headless body, buried it in the earth, and a few nights after that the grave was torn wide open and the body without the head of that greedy man was gone.

"Some spoke, some thought, and some guessed, and it all came to this. The body of that godless man belonged to the witches. They robbed the grave and buried the body under a young elm to grow a witch tree as a marker for the buried treasure. A witch tree as a marker for the witches and as a means to torture the dead man for the evil deeds he did.

"That witch tree grew different from any tree around here. It was like a man, with two thick trunk-legs comin' from the earth spread apart. Thick branches like giant hands and giant fingers wide apart reached out and pointed the way for the witches to find the buried silver.

"On stormy nights the witches 'd scream in the branches and tear 'em in tatters, and that'd torment without end the evil man lying buried under the witch tree for what he'd done on earth.

"That witch tree of the ungodly man stood there seven times seven years till his time was up, when the Lord forgave him for his sins.

"Then the witch tree died and the witches could not torment the mean man's soul any more.

"But a good mess o' that silver is still hid in the deep ground somewhere round this part of the country, waiting to be found by a man with the Lord's own luck and a fool's wisdom. For, you know, a drop of luck is worth a barrel o' wisdom."

Hi-ho, the Mosquitoes of New Jersey!

THERE has even been great arguments between Jerseyites and Yorkers as to who had the best mosquitoes in the land. Yorkers proudly tell of the skeeters with the double stingers up in the Adirondack Mountains, and Jersey men proudly say they are called the Mosquito State and the skeeters of their swamps could paralyze man and beast with a single sting. No matter what tale a Yorker tells, a Jerseyite has one better, and the best of all is what their skeeters did in the early days.

In the days of the Swedes and the Dutch, the mosquitoes in Jersey were the size of swallows and fierce as eagles. One bite of those mosquitoes, and a Dutchman or a Swede or any animal would turn numb as from a snake bite, and when they zoomed at night it was like the roaring of the sea.

Once the people combined to drive these skeeters away. The great battle took place in Bergen County, but the skeeters won out, and the Dutch and Swedes went back to their toil and the skeeters to their stings.

The Indians in those days were much wiser. They kept these bird-sized mosquitoes in their wigwams and trained them to hunt, just as they did their dogs and horses. They trained them to bite the deer and bears; the game became paralyzed, and then it was a simple matter to shoot them with arrows.

One day the Indians caught some mosquitoes that had lived with the white settlers and found that the sting from skeeters bred on white men's blood was more poisonous than those fed on red men's blood. From then on the red men trained only mosquitoes from swamps and fields of the white men and gained a good deal thereby.

Those biting insects could not only make a deer stand in its tracks but could stop a rooster from flying and a cow from mooing. Now, whenever some Indian was too lazy to roam the country for game, he'd send his trained skeeters to a Dutch or Swedish farm to sting an animal into silence, drag it off, and feast on it.

Dutchman and Swedes met in council to retaliate.

"We want no wars," said one good Dutchman, "but I think we ought to show these thieving savages that we are not afraid of them. Why not take the favorite horse of the Indian chief, hold it as a hostage, and when he wants it back we'll return it only on condition that they stop the stingers from attacking our cattle and hens and geese?"

The word was said and the deed was done.

But when the chief found the settlers had stolen his finest horse, he declared a bloody war against them.

Dutch and Swedes oiled their blunderbusses and polished up their pikes and daggers. One fine day the two armies were ranged against each other to decide the question of horse and skeeters.

The Indians yelled and fired their arrows, the settlers roared and fired their guns, and very soon the Indians were near beaten. But, alas, it was only a short victory.

The wily Indian chief, seeing the way the battle went, now called on his reserves. They let loose their trained mosquitoes held in green, twig baskets and the skeeters attacked Dutchmen and Swedes with their paralyzing stingers.

In a short time not a white soldier could move hand or foot; they could only talk.

They cried and begged for peace, which the Indians quickly granted on payment of certain things.

The Jersey settlers were ashamed for the world to know how they were beaten by mosquitoes, but when they heard that their neighbors in Delaware had given up their finest fort after a two-week attack by Delaware mosquitoes they weren't ashamed at all. They swallowed their pride and drank and ate heartily and said that shame is the mark of base men. The more they ate and the more they drank, the more they believed that they should be proud of their mosquitoes and not ashamed.

That's why Jersey men are ever ready to dispute with Yorkers as to who has the finest mosquitoes in the land.

The Strange Trial

THE people of Mount Holly in New Jersey were in a great to-do, nagging and bickering, as is too often the way with people. And what do you think their nagging and bickering was about? Why, nought else than whether Mistress Betty and Master Paul were witches practicing the black arts and doing harm to men and beasts.

Many accused them, while some said it was foolish blather of unthinking minds. But, as often is the case, those who cried loudest with least sense won out.

They brought the two before the judge, and Mistress Deborah and Master Cabbot were the worst accusers.

"They make sheep dance in the moonlight when the black clouds run wild in the sky," cried Mistress Deborah.

"They make hogs speak vile words and sing squeaky psalms," said Master Cabbot.

"They spoil the churning butter, bring disease to healthy cattle, ride horses so they are wet and brambly."

This and many other things these two held against Mistress Betty and Master Paul. They demanded the two should be hung on the gallows.

It was of little avail that some who did not believe this cried out against it. In the end the judge had to say the two should be tried against the weight of the Holy Bible or by water.

Mistress Betty and Master Paul pleaded their innocence, but it did them little good. In the end they said they would undergo any trial if their two worst accusers, Mistress Deborah and Master Paul, would do the same.

The judge, a just man who held "the best way to burn witches was without faggots," said:

"I see no harm in putting to the same trial the loudest accusers, Mistress Deborah and Master Cabbot, with the two accused as witches. Since Mistress Deborah and Master Cabbot are not witches, no test will hurt them."

The people thought this strange, but there was no arguing with the judge, and the date for the queer trial was set.

A more fair day the Lord could not have chosen. All was peace and beauty, sunshine and green, save the people crying for the trial of the witches.

There was a great crowd in the town to see if Mistress Betty and Master Paul were innocent or guilty.

First the judge ordered the sheriff to examine the accused to see if they had any weights on them that might outweigh the Bible. Most of all they looked for pins, which are common things used by those in league with the Devil. The big Bible belonging to the judge was brought out solemnly by the minister. He carried it to the gallows, where a giant pair of scales had been set up. Then the prisoners came, and after them the two accusers. The Bible was put on one side of the scale, and then Master Paul was asked to step on the other side of the scale. Every mother's child there craned his neck to see if the Bible full of holiness would outweigh the partner of the Devil. But, wonder of wonders, when Master Paul got on the scale, bang!, the scale came down with a thud and the holy Bible flew high in the air!

Next, Mistress Betty went on the scale and . . . the very same thing happened!

When Master Cabbot and Mistress Deborah went on it, it was no different!

The judge was silent, but the crowd roared.

"They are witches just the same; try them by water. They are in league with the fiend." The few who were against it, saying the trial proved the accused innocent, were not even heard.

So the four were taken to the water.

First they were stripped of most of their clothes. Then, one after the other, Mistress Betty, Master Paul, Mistress Deborah, and Master Cabbot, were thrown into the water. Though the sheriff tried again and again to force them down, it was of little avail. All four, the accusers and accused, came up just the same, and in the end the good judge decided that Mistress Betty and Master Paul were innocent of witchcraft, since they were no different than innocent Mistress Deborah and Master Cabbot.

From that day onward there wasn't another trial of witchcraft in Mount Holly in New Jersey.

Jonas and the Sturgeon

JONAS was a hunter, Jonas was a fisherman, he was six-foot five in his stocking feet, and could bend iron rods like soft tree twigs. He could outrun a fox in a ten-hour run, and he hated the German Hessians so much he trapped 'em and destroyed 'em in the great war for freedom.

When the war was over folks made him whipper-in of the fox-hunt club, for he could follow a fox on foot better than hunters a-horse.

One fine day he went fishing in wide Timber Creek, and soon he felt a pull on his line the like he never felt before. There was a fish for certain, and he put up a battle fiercer than a fighting whale in the ocean. Churning waves rose sixty feet high, and the boat twisted and turned like a snake on fire. In the end Jonas had that fish high enough to see it was a sturgeon unlike any sturgeon in the rivers of America.

He was near twenty-two feet from head to tail, with ten rows of shields on the sides. The plate on his head looked like armor, and his snout was seven feet long.

But the fish was not caught yet! First he raced through

the water like lightning in a hurry. Next there was a pulling match between Jonas and the sturgeon that is spoken about to this very day whenever good men gather in Cumberland County and Gloucester County.

Jonas pulled up, the sturgeon down. The sturgeon leaped twenty feet in the air, then down, and Jonas took a nose dive. They pulled and they hauled, they tugged and they tore. Jersey men on the shores screamed and roared. In the end Jonas had the sturgeon high on the boat but hanging ten feet out in the water. The sturgeon's tail floundered and flounced in that water so fiercely, it drove the boat along like a house afire. Jonas was soon ninety miles from his home and thought it was time to return, so he cut the line loose and cried:

"You an' I are in the same class. I'd like to know you better, and I know you'd enjoy my company."

From then on Jonas and the sturgeon were good friends. Jonas fed him meat and played with him on the river. He thought he had him tamed so he would behave right and proper, but Jonas was wrong. Never trust a sturgeon.

One day, it was the twenty-third of June, Jonas went out riding on the river with his best girl. He harnessed the sturgeon to the stern of the boat, aiming to have some fun with his best girl, and with the sturgeon, too.

The great fish was also in a merry mood. He had heard from some fish about the "sleigh rides" men took on boats out in Nantucket, and he made up his mind to show what a sturgeon could do in New Jersey.

He shot down the river like a streak of greased lightning and twisted on the sides lickety split. Then he flashed in and out and all around, in and out and all around till they reached a little bridge on which some cows were passing.

Jonas tried his best to steer his sea horse off, but, crash, it went into the bridge, and the heaviest cow fell plump into the water, drowning in a trice!

Jonas thought it was high time to quit, and the sturgeon was just as glad. He dived down in the water and had a feast of the freshest cow meat he'd ever had. It was the best he'd ever tasted.

It tasted so good he wanted fresh, raw beef meat every day. Jonas soon found the sturgeon would not eat the tidbits of meat and bread he brought him, and the farmers in Gloucester and Cumberland counties found their Jersey cows and calves were disappearing! It got so bad the farmers sent out vigilantes to catch the robbers, offering a great reward.

Farmers watched in the pastures, boys watched in the meadows; hunters watched in the woods, and fishermen watched on the rivers, and one fine night a fisherman and a farmer saw a sight 'd make a blind man see.

Suddenly from out Timber Creek a giant sturgeon full over twenty feet leaped in the air right on the river bank. Its scales glistened green in the moonlight as it slithered along the grassy bank. Sliding, gliding, and wriggling, that sturgeon went through a meadow and a field and reached a pasture where a herd of fine, dark-brown Jersey cows, who give the fattest milk in the world, were lying in the lush grass, chewing in happy silence.

That giant sturgeon slid along to where a calf was lying off from the others—and, call me King Solomon!, it opened its jaws, got hold of the calf's head, and began pulling it along the grass at a breakneck speed!

Fisherman and farmer raised a hue and a cry and ran after that fish cow-thief.

The sturgeon dropped his prey and made for the river so speedily the men couldn't get a shot at him!

All the countryside was roused, and Jonas was hailed to the law, for he was held responsible for his pet sturgeon.

The judge listened to the arguments and said Jonas had to pay the farmers for the loss of their cattle. Since so many of them were lost, Jonas was a poor man for the rest of his life. That made Jonas mad as a hornet. He took his trusty gun and cried out, "If I must take the blame, I might as well earn the game."

He prowled along the river in the black night and also when the moon was shining high, but that sturgeon who heard Jonas the great hunter was after him was mighty wary. But Jonas didn't give up, and one night he was rewarded.

He was hidden in the bushes along the river bank, and the wind was blowing toward him so the sturgeon couldn't smell him. The fish came out, hoping for a stray cow or calf, but instead of that . . . crack! There was a shot like thunder, and the sturgeon lost his tail, for at the instant that Jonas fired, the sturgeon put down its head and stuck out its tail.

The giant fish wasn't dead, but he was without a tail. And that was enough for him. Whoever heard of a sturgeon without a tail! What is more, he needed his tail to navigate both in water and on the land!

From that day on that sturgeon was never seen again, but Jonas had to pay the damages just the same.

That's what happened to Jonas and the sturgeon, and it's a good lesson for those who'd make a pet of a sturgeon in New Jersey.

The Foe in the Dark

IN Bergen County, on Cherry Hill and nearby, the British and the German Hessians were battling our loyal men during the Revolution. But no matter how fierce the battling, how great the woe, the American boys were ever ready for fun and frolic and a little joy. So whenever there was a chance the good Jersey Blues, as the Jersey fighting men were called, would leave Fort Patriot at Cherry Hill and go to the old stone tavern for a little merrymaking. There, sweethearts, friends, and parents of the loyal fighters waited with burning cheeks and beating hearts to steal a few hours of pleasure in talk and dance.

One Saturday night, when the wind blew wild and the rain hissed through the leaves, a troup of young Jersey Blues left Fort Patriot to go to the stone tavern.

They walked singly, Indian file, Cornelius Berdan leading. The wind and rain whipped their faces, and the shrubs and twigs danced a crazy dance.

They had gone about halfway, when Cornelius turned to the man behind him and said, "John, one of us should stay here and watch against surprise attacks from British or Hessians."

"We need have no fear. Henry Ackerman, a true American, spread the word in Hackensack that we are going to the dance, and friends are spying on the lobster-backs and Hessian pigs so that we are not surprised."

They trudged on, and soon they saw the twinkling light of the inn. No star in heaven was more inviting than those lights from afar.

In the large room, girls and their mothers, fathers and their friends were waiting eagerly. Soon wet rain, wind, and war were forgotten in the warmth of love and friendship and merrymaking.

They were all so busy, no one saw Fritz the stableman mount his horse. He went into the dark night riding like the very Devil with the cloven hoof, through lanes and ditches, through shrubs and woods, until he reached the British camp right outside of Hackensack.

The British knew he was a spy, and he told of the Americans who were at the inn and could easily be captured.

The commander gave orders at once for the attack. An equal number of British and German Hessians were ordered to surround the tavern from different sides, to make certain the American soldiers couldn't escape.

So one half came along from the Hackensack River and the other straight from Hackensack town.

But the good Lord watches over those who battle for a righteous cause.

A baker of the town, working for the British in order to spy upon them for the Americans, learned quickly of the preparations, and he gave the news to loyal friends. One of them set out a-horse at once to warn our boys of the peril.

He rode as if for life, and in a short time, wet and weary, he reached the tavern, where all were gay and merry.

He told quickly that the Germans and British were on the way, and the Jersey Blues swiftly bade parents and sweethearts good-by. Then they set off singly to return to Fort Patriot. They got back safely, with only a few scratches from brush and bramble, for the night was as dark as Egypt.

Meanwhile the British and the Hessians, from opposite sides, each under their commanders, plodded through mud and rain, through wilds and winds.

The nearer they came to the inn, the more cautious they were, for they didn't want a single American to escape.

The rain came thick as clover in a clover year, the wind howled, and you couldn't see a foot ahead. Both British and Germans were getting nearer to the inn.

Soon they were quite close, each force coming directly against the other. Suddenly the British heard a noise different from the falling rain and the wind in the leaves.

They heard the Hessians coming.

The Hessians, too, heard a noise that was different from before. It was the sound of the British going through brush and briar.

It was too black to see anything clearly ahead, and

each force thought the other was the force of the Americans leaving—perhaps on a warning.

Each began to fire wildly at the other. Then they came to blows with guns and bayonets.

So they kept at each other until a lobsterback lieutenant nailed a Hessian with the butt of his gun and the Hessian cried for mercy in German words.

The British captain then knew they were fighting their own allies and not the Americans.

They stopped. The dead were buried; the wounded and the living started back from whence they had come, a beaten lot, wet and weary.

Folks around Hackensack heard the tale, laughed, and said the enemy now could learn a little wisdom from their pain and folly.

The Young Witch-Horse

THERE lived a young farmer in New Jersey, his name was James, who was as handsome as could be. He was tall and had brown eyes, his hair was curly, and he had winning ways. And he had plenty of courage besides.

Now, James loved horses more than anything else. Horses to ride and horses to walk; horses to race and horses to pet. He had plenty of them in his stalls, and he took as much care of them as he did of himself. He combed them and curried them and shod them.

The blacksmith, a fine fellow, had the prettiest wife in town. She had black eyes and black hair, and folks said there was gypsy blood in her veins. Soon James and the blacksmith and his wife were very good friends.

James was there evenings, and they would all talk of this and that, but mostly of the strange goings on in the valley. There were witches at work!

Animals turned sick; young children were ailing, and no doctoring could help; often all the churning would not turn cream into butter.

Folks were scared and watched warily.

James and the blacksmith and his beautiful gypsy-looking wife spoke about it one night, but she only laughed and cried, "What if there are witches hereabouts? They don't do half the harm that's done by good folks."

"That's not true, and you know it well," James said warmly. "I don't like witches, and we should treat 'em as they do in Salem in New England."

But the blacksmith did not believe in hanging people. His pretty, young wife laughed, showing her straight white teeth, and said, "James, maybe if you meet a handsome witch you'll think differently."

She looked at him with her jet-black eyes until he felt she was looking right through him.

James went home thinking of witches and the blacksmith's wife. He felt queerer than he'd ever felt before; the cries of the whippoorwills and katydids had a strange sound in the white night.

He passed by a bog and looked into the water. A pair of black eyes looked at him . . . and the bullfrogs were booming croaking laughter!

"I am bewitched," he said, and tried to keep his head clear.

He went to sleep and slept right well, forgetting his silly thoughts. But at midnight he was awakened by a woman's mocking laughter.

A woman's hand held his, and he was whisked out of his bed into the open under the white moon. They flew on till they came to a wide green, where he saw shadowy creatures and heard the scraping of a fiddle. On a black pine stump sat a tall man, a dark cloak covering all of him save his head that had two little horns on it.

James knew at once it was the Devil, but he did not know who the shadowy girl was who'd brought him through the air. She had a gray cloak all over, and only now and then he saw two jet-black eyes which he thought he had seen before.

The creatures on the green began swirling to the tune of the violin, and the girl who'd brought him began whirling with James the same as the others. Try as he would, he could not stop. On and around they went, with never a rest.

Suddenly there was the crowing of a cock and, whisht!, his black-eyed partner rushed him through the air and he was home, tired and worn out.

He slept but little that night nor many a night then-after. Every midnight the young black-eyed witch came and whisked him off to the green to dance.

She never spoke to him, nor did the others. Just danced, nothing else. He never saw her, either, only her coal-black eyes.

Often he cried he did not want to go. Then she'd laugh, and a familiar voice 'd say, "It's fun to dance with a nice young man," and whisk him through the air.

Folks noticed how wan and worn James looked.

One day when he was in the tavern he told his closest friend what happened every night. The fellow knew all about witches, so he said:

"The next time the witch comes to take you to her Sabbath dance, take along a halter. When you see your chance, bridle her with it, and then you'll be master over her, and she will do your bidding instead of you hers. You'll be able to ride her instead of she, you."

The next night James lay down to sleep in his coat with a halter hidden under it. No sooner did the witch get hold of his hand and they were out and up in the air, than he threw the halter over her.

Then the strangest thing in all the world happened. When the halter was on her neck the witch . . . turned into a fine black steed!

James was puzzled, as anyone would be, but, loving horse flesh and feeling the fine horse under him, he rode her through the moonlit roads and then into the stable.

First thing the next morning James went into the stable to see the new horse. There it stood, a fine, coal-black mare with silky mane, but he noticed she was unshod.

He took her at once to his friend the blacksmith.

The blacksmith brought out some iron horseshoes and put them in the fire. When the fire was glowing red he took one with his pliers, went up to the mare, and raised her front hoof and put the red-hot shoe to it. But no sooner did the sizzling metal touch the hoof than there was a great flame in the smithy, the room filled with smoke that had a strange odor, and there before them was no horse . . . but the blacksmith's black-eyed wife, a deep fresh burn on her hand. Her eyes were flashing fury.

She ran out screaming, and the blacksmith roared for her never to come back.

She never came back, and James was never plagued by witches again.

The Treasure
Under the Tree

In Burlington there stood a buttonwood tree,
And around it the witches dance merrily;
And in Burlington there stood a walnut tree,
Where the pirates buried their great treasury.

FOLK tell strange tales about these trees, and here is one that I like best.

Among the witches who rode the storms there were old dame Brady, the worst witch in the town, and young Ann-of-the-Sea, and a lovelier witch there never was seen. She had gray eyes and jet-black hair, and she wore a great silver belt wrought by skillful hands.

Ann-of-the-Sea had a sweetheart, but she saw little of him. He was a Spanish don pledged to serve Old Blackbeard, the pirate, for seven years, to rob and kill and sail the seas. They sailed and they robbed and they hid their loot in caves and under trees and then went pirating again. But what made the Spanish don happiest was to come to Burlington, where he could see his Ann with the dark-gray eyes and the blue-black hair walking along the shore like a queen to a coronation. Every time they were together the don swore they'd soon be together forever, that he would give up his life on the sea and stay in Burlington.

Came a day when Captain Blackbeard and the Spanish don plundered a large ship and made a great haul, so they decided to bury it with more care than usual, where no man could touch it but themselves.

"Why not somewhere along the Delaware," said the don, "say, in Burlington?"

The pirate captain had nothing against that, but he knew full well why the Spanish don wanted to go to New Jersey. All the crew knew that the gentleman from Spain loved Ann-of-the-Sea and was ready to leave his pirate life and wed her when the proper time would come. Captain Blackbeard knew that, too, and didn't like it a bit. He was afraid that the two would betray him, and he made up his mind to end this affair in his own particular way.

He sailed his vessel up the Delaware, dodging in and out the shore not to be seen, and one wild, late afternoon they landed right near Burlington Village.

The Spanish don asked at once to leave the vessel, but the captain told him to stay with the men while he went to find the proper place to hide the rich loot.

Captain Blackbeard went ashore, went all around the buttonwood tree, and around the walnut tree, and around the house where Ann lived, and nobody will ever know what he did there.

When he came back to the ship he said he had found the right and proper place to bury the treasure and now the don could go ashore, but Blackbeard asked him to return as soon as possible, for he wanted to bury the gold and silver and jewels as soon as it could be done.

The Spanish don went ashore and turned his steps to Dame Brady's house where his love Ann lived. It was a way off from the town, and the walking wasn't easy. A wild wind screeched in the trees, and there was lightning in the sky.

He came to the house and knocked on the door. Not a sound from within. The big black dog who loved both his mistress and her lover howled mournfully and whined and whimpered, as if trying to tell the don what had happened.

Again and again the don knocked at the door, then he broke it in. But no Ann was there—no one was there. Black fear and black anger helped him little—the house was empty, empty as death.

He went back to the ship, the black dog following him, and never said a word to a man. The dog growled at the captain, but Blackbeard just laughed and gave orders for the crew to get the caskets ready to bury them where none but themselves would find them.

There were two heavy chests, and each took six men to carry. Captain Blackbeard walked in front, the Spanish don behind, followed by the big black dog. So they came to a giant walnut tree.

The captain stopped, and so did the crew, and they began digging in the earth. Though the wind howled in the branches and lightning flashed in the sky, the captain ordered a deep hole to be dug, deeper than just to hold the two chests—deep enough for a man to stand in. The chests were lowered, a broad flat stone was placed over them, and the pirates picked shovels of earth to cover it all. Said Captain Blackbeard:

"Not yet!"

The men dropped their shovels, and no one looked at another nor at the captain.

Blackbeard looked slowly from one to another but mostly at the Spanish don, who had never said a word since he came back to the ship.

"Who'll guard the gold and jewels?" Captain Blackbeard said. "It must be watched by a dead man if we ever want it back."

There was a flash of lightning in that dry storm, and the pirates' faces shone green in the light. Not a man moved, not a man opened his mouth.

Again Captain Blackbeard said:

"One must guard this gold against any but us taking it. Who'll guard it? One must be buried with the gold so no one but ourselves can get it."

Not a man moved. But when he said it for the third time, the Spanish don came forward.

Ann was gone! He might as well go, too.

"I've nothing to live for," he said, "I am sick of robbing and looting. I want to stay here."

Captain Blackbeard, a black smile on his face, raised

his pistol that was loaded with a charmed bullet made of silver. He fired, and the bullet went clear through the Spanish don's head. There was no wound, no drop of blood, so the don could battle any mortal who would try to lift the treasure from under that walnut tree.

The big black dog howled fiercely, and Captain Black-beard sent a silver bullet through him, too. Then the pirate crew lowered the don and his dog in the earth, standing them upright on the chests. And there they have stood since, guarding that gold in Burlington so not a mortal soul could touch it, though many a one has tried. For no treasure can be touched that's guarded by the dead who've been shot with a charmed silver bullet.

But on stormy nights, when Ann and her witches come flying through the town, the black dog and the Spanish don can be seen running through Wood Street in Bur-lington, New Jersey, where that great walnut tree was standing.

I scratched the justice's swine on the head—
    When he wakes in the morning he'll find him dead.
And I saw the pirates land on the shore,
    Loaded with gold, but crimson with gore.

The Seven Sisters

Seven brave maids
Sat on seven broad beds
Braiding seven broad braids;
Said I to the seven brave maids
Braiding seven broad braids:
"Braid broad braids, brave maids!"

THAT'S what the seven brave Jenkin sisters in Bergen, from Frankie the youngest to Mary Eliza the eldest, did. They braided and baked and did many other things besides. All went well until one sad day their dear mother died. They wept and wailed, but time and work, tending the house and their dear father brought back cheer to their faces, though there still was sorrow in their hearts.

The seven sisters grew older and worked harder, and their father took joy in their sight and pride in their work.

One lovely evening Jeremiah, the dear father of the seven sisters, called them into the front parlor with the red carpet and flowery lamps.

"Dear daughters mine," said he, "you are beautiful and have been dutiful. No father could wish for finer children or more meritorious. Now I shall reward you.

"I have built seven fine houses on the crest of the hill that looks down on the meadows, on the great cities, and the river full of sailing ships. Each house is exactly like the other. All are the same size with the same number of chambers. Each is furnished alike with fine tables, beds, and bureaus. To each of you I give one house. Besides, here's ten thousand dollars for each of you to reward you for your faithfulness and obedience.

"Now, each of you go to your own home and live there happily."

"Why, dear father," cried Mary Eliza the eldest, "why, dear father, must we leave the home where we are so contented?"

"Because, fair daughter mine," said Jeremiah, "I am about to take another wife unto myself to take the place of your dear mother."

The seven sisters were angry and sad, but Jeremiah was a firm man, and in the end the seven thought it best to take their money and their homes rather than live with a stepmother.

So each moved into her own sweet house while their dear father got himself a new wife.

At first the seven sisters were lonely in their new homes, but soon each found pleasure tending to herself, seeing friends, and visiting one another.

They lived contentedly, never thinking of husbands to destroy their tranquillity. Sharp tongues called them old maids, but that was just green jealousy.

Each house had bells with strings running into the next house, so the seven sisters could talk to one another, whenever they wanted to, by the tinkling of the bells.

Frankie, the youngest and the prettiest, lived right in the middle. Mary Eliza lived at one end, the next eldest at the other. Each succeeding in age lived one house up toward Frankie, so that she, the youngest, was protected on each side by elder sisters.

Now, one rainy night Frankie and Mary Eliza went to Mister Meyer's store to buy some things they needed. Mister Meyer was there, and so was pink-faced George Lilly, the new clerk just come from Merrie England.

George looked at Frankie, and he fell in love as no man ever did before. He offered her an apple as red as his face, but she giggled and would not take it. But that did not daunt George Lilly just come from England. He swore in his heart he would marry that pretty girl if he had to battle for her like St. George of old.

Though he knew not Frankie's name nor home, he looked for her all over. But as luck would have it, Frankie came into the store again one day with Mary Eliza.

By then George Lilly was the owner of the place, and when he saw Frankie for the second time he loved her even more. He learned her name, she came often, they spoke together, and one fine day he went to visit her.

The six sisters were all a-flutter, but Frankie spoke innocently and said he had only brought back an umbrella she'd left behind—and had invited her to church on Sunday.

Mary Eliza and the five sisters stormed and blustered, but Sunday came, and bright and early George Lilly was there dressed in checkered pants and tall top hat, unlike any clothes worn by any good American.

Do you think Frankie would go to church with a man dressed like an Englishman in a picture book? Not she. She sent him home and told him to return the next Sunday dressed in good American clothes, and then she'd go to church with him.

God's day came, and so did faithful George, dressed in the best suit that could be found between Bergen and New York City.

To church they went on Sunday, to church they went another Sunday, and many Sundays after, until they went one Sunday when the wedding bells rang for them.

Frankie walked in white, George, in black, and the six sisters followed. So did their dear father Jeremiah and his newly wedded wife, as well as many friends.

Frankie and George lived in their little house, three maiden sisters on each side, but George didn't like this at all. Nor did his good wife Frankie.

So clever George invited his gentlemen friends to his home. Soon, one after another, the other sisters were married, even to Mary Eliza, the eldest, who had sworn no man would ever touch the hem of her skirt.

Then never again did

> Seven brave maids sit on seven broad beds
> Braiding seven broad braids.

Instead, the seven brave sister maids baked broad breads, cooked good meals, and tended to their homes and children, as all brave married women should do.

The Gunsmith and the Maiden

YOU always hear tales of heroism and bloodshed in the Revolutionary War, but I'll tell you one of love and smartness that'll bring a smile to your face and a thrill to your heart.

In those days loyal Americans not only had to fight the British but Hessian Germans and American traitors, too. They had to fight them on the battlefield and in the home as well, for the enemy was not only killing men but robbing homes.

Now, when the news came to Freehold, in New Jersey, that the British and their henchmen were coming for attack, most loyal men of freedom went into the fields, while the others hid cattle and horse in neighboring swamps so the enemy would not get them.

Young Alex the blacksmith, busy from dawn to night repairing guns and cannons for our army, took his fine horse and rode it into the swamp nearby, where he was certain the redcoats would not find it.

Aaron Davis, from a farm a ways off, sent his cows with

his young daughter, Ann, to hide them from the enemy.

Ann was pretty, and Ann was sweet, and Ann had plenty of courage. She led the beasts with care and caution, through woods and meadows, resting them at times. Deeper and deeper she went, and soon she heard the dull roar of cannons from the distance.

Men were battling, but she had her duty, too. The cattle must not feed the foreign soldiers.

She had gone on cautiously for a time when she stopped and listened. There was a crashing noise in the brush and trees! Maybe it was the British or Hessian foragers!

There was the sound of horses! She did not know it was only Alex on his horse trying to find a hiding place.

She must lead the cattle the other way! She turned them and ran them as fast as she could. Brambles tore her legs and clothes, and branches whipped her face, but she went on without heeding them.

On her lovely black hair she wore a fine chip-hat made of braided cloth, and as she ran and stumbled a branch caught her hat and began to unbraid it.

Alex with his horse were now right nearby, breaking through trees and brush. Suddenly he heard a tramping, crashing noise. He was sure there was a troop of lobster-backs or maybe Hessians coming through the woods.

The noise stopped suddenly, and all was still. Alex tied his horse and made his way cautiously to learn the cause of the crashing.

Ann, finding the braids of her chip-hat unraveling,

turned about to get the braid. She was a thrifty girl and would use the material again.

Right then Alex came up the same way, and there, instead of lobsterback or Hessian, he saw a lovely girl all confused and blustering, trying to get the braid caught in the branches without tearing it.

She looked up at the sound of the noise, and there before her was a tall young man all flushed and flustered.

The two came toward each other and stopped short. They looked at each other, and Alex's heart was lost. Said he with a Scotch burr in his words:

"Whatever are ye doin' in these parts?"

Ann was quick and replied, "Maybe the same thing ye are doing. How is it ye are not amongst the fighting men? Ye don't look like a lobsterback or a Hessian or . . ."

"I am a gunsmith right now, workin' hard repairin' guns and cannons for Americans to use. Y' can't fight a war without guns an' cannons."

"I'm glad you told me that. I'm glad ye aren't shirking your duty as a true American. I was hiding cattle for my father so the enemy would not have food to fight."

"I was hidin' my horse so the British would not get it. We were both doing the very same thing. What's your name, lassie?"

"Ann. What's yours?"

"Alexander Low. Now we can both hide our animals together, and you can watch 'em while I'll return to see if I can be of help to the fighting men."

But he did not go at once. They spoke of this and that,

as ever happens when the right young man meets the right young girl.

In the end Alex went while Ann remained to watch horse and cows.

After a time he came back and said they could return. Together they went, close to each other, till they reached a road where they had to part. But it was not parting for long.

Alex and Ann met many a time until they met not to part. They were married and lived happy ever after.

Pirate Yan Yost of Communipaw

THE Wild Goose Tavern, in Communipaw in New Jersey, had an evil name, for there Yan Yost Vanderscamp ruled with a bloody fist. He was a pirate and a robber with no fear of God or the Devil. He robbed on high seas and cheated on dry land.

The good Dutch burghers were scared of him, and the English sailors were trying to have him hung on the gallows on Gibbet Island, where most pirates had their end.

The lieutenant of this pirate was a giant called Pluto, a black man who was as much a robber as his master. Some Dutch folks and even some English said they had seen two little horns sticking from his woolly head and that he wore extra-large boots which could easily hide a cloven hoof.

One night, when the crew were sitting, carousing, in the taproom of the Wild Goose Tavern, Captain Yan Yost came in and shouted, "I want three men who aren't easily scared for a little work and a rich reward. Half goes to them who'll do it quick."

More than three rose at once, and Yan Yost chose those he thought best fit and said:

"There's a boat on the way from New York Bay to Gibbet Island laden with caskets of Holland and Madeira and port. Just what we could use ourselves and sell at a good price. You'll take your boat and bring in the prize. The crew you can drop in the middle of the sea to find their own way back, or maybe they'd like to stay down below."

The three set out with sail and oars, but this time they guessed all wrong. The boat with the cargo of wines and spirits was manned by British and Portuguese men who didn't mind a scuffle at all, and in the end the three pirates were tied hand and foot and on their way to New York City.

Their trial was swift, and two days later they were dangling high with rope and chain on Gallows Hill in Gibbet Island, right outside of New York.

Yan Yost and his crew in Communipaw learned it quick, but it did not worry them overmuch. There were always new men ready to join the sea wolves. But they kept clear of Gibbet Island, where their boon companions were swinging high in the wind.

One day, soon after, they robbed an unprotected vessel and set the crew adrift. They were on their way to Communipaw, to the Wild Goose Tavern, to divide and hide their loot. A wild wind was blowing and, work as they would, their skiff steered right toward Gibbet Island, where their three companions were still swinging in clanking chorus.

"Steer away from there," roared Captain Yan Yost.

"Are you scared?" said Pluto, the mate. "You've always said you didn't fear man or Devil, so you can't be scared of men of our own crew. They're just waving greetings."

Yan Yost felt cold all over, but, not to show it, he bellowed, "I scared! Y' black son o' the Devil, I'll show y'," and he shouted in the wind to the swinging men, "Ho, there! ye three, when y're through with your rounds tonight, come to the tavern and join me for a drink."

The answer was a clattering and clanking, or it might have been laughter to any who listened sharply.

At midnight, when the wind still roared and the rain still fell, the pirate boat landed at Communipaw, and the pirates lugged their loot in the stormy night to the Wild Goose Tavern.

There was a light in the room on the floor above the taproom, and hoarse voices could be heard.

Yan Yost ran up in a bound to see who dared intrude in his home.

He opened the door, and by the eerie, waving light of a candle on the table he saw the three pirates from the gallows with halter and chain still on their necks and wrists. They sat, with gray pewter tankards in their hands, looking straight at Yan Yost with green and glassy eyes.

"Come, Captain," they said hoarsely. "Y' invited us, and we've come. We never refused any order y' gave us even when it landed us on the gallows." All three laughed.

Captain Yan Yost fell back from the door.

"Y' can't run away from us," one of the three said with a laugh. "Don't be scared; don't be scared of us. We've come as y' bid."

Captain Yan Yost stumbled backward, looking almost as green and black as the pirate cadavers. He stumbled on the landing and then fell down the flight of stairs with a fierce thud. His men ran up and saw their captain was dead.

They looted the place and made off quick as fire, leaving no trace or track.

When the body of the pirate was found, the good people of Communipaw buried it in holy ground, but it did the pirate robber little good. On stormy nights with howling winds, there was ever heard around the Wild Goose Tavern the roistering, roaring voices of the three pirates and their captain. And mariners passing Gibbet Island on the way to the Battery in New York saw strange, blue lights flitting in the air and heard the clanking chains of those who were hung there for their misdeeds.

The Saga
of Stretch Garrison

YOU may talk of the sailor-cowboy who sailed up Nantucket in Massachusetts, but he hasn't a lick on the farmer-hunter-sailor who lived on the Maurice River in New Jersey.

Stretch Garrison was his name, and no man was handier at the barn, quicker on the hunt, or smarter with a boat.

One day Stretch was fishing on the lovely Maurice River that runs in from the Delaware Bay. Suddenly he felt a fierce tug on his line. He pulled and he pulled, and no man in all Jersey could pull harder than Stretch, and soon he saw on his line a monstracious, long-nosed shark with white, gleaming teeth. Stretch pulled hard, the shark pulled harder. Stretch roared, the shark began plowing the river, racing like mad and making furrows fifty yards on each side. But Stretch wouldn't let go. The shark kept on, on up, mile after mile. There was little water that summer up the Maurice River, but the shark kept on plowing in the mud full five miles, right to Stretch's own landing place. By then the giant fish was tired and laid down to rest. Stretch fed him and harnessed him and petted him, and soon he rode him up and down the river just as he did his horse.

Jersey folks along the banks, and folks way inland, heard of it, came to see the marvel, and said it was the eighth wonder of the world. Even the gentry in Washington heard about it, senators and congressmen.

So they gave Stretch the job of carrying the U.S. mail up and down the Maurice River. Stretch and the shark did a faithful job for many a year, until the shark grew old and said he could do no more. Then Stretch let him go off to sea and die a good fish's death among his relatives and friends.

Stretch was now a famous man, satisfied with life and with himself. But he was a restless critter. Said he to himself one day:

"I've done a mighty good American job on the sea with my horse-shark, now let me see what I can do on my green land. I've neglected my farm for many a year riding up and down the river on my horse-shark; now I've got to tend cows and chickens that have gone to seed and sorrow."

From morn to night Stretch worked in barns and fields, and soon they were green and growing so that it was good to the eyes.

Now, Stretch was a mighty smart farmer, just as he was a mighty smart fishing man, and he began to look around how best to improve his farm, since he wanted to spend his ending years on it.

One fine day his good horses went lame, and there was a stretch of plowing to do that would take at least a week.

What to do? Horses were dear 's gold nuggets, and Stretch didn't want to throw away his hard-earned money. He had some cows that weren't good milkers, so he hitched 'em to the plow, held a fork of hay three feet in front, and kept on walking steadily. The cows followed the smell of the hay in front, and they plowed up the land behind.

So Stretch worked his land without horses, and every farmer round Cumberland County was green with envy.

His horses got no better, and the cows weren't strong enough to pull loads of wood or loads of manure. So the sailor-farmer-hunter set his thinking-pan to work to get him a horse without paying for it.

Stretch had a pet rooster named Big Boy, and a finer rooster there wasn't in all the country wide. His comb was red as the rising sun, and when he crowed, pigeons fell off their perches.

Big Boy's feed was on top o' the feed box, and he had to jump to get it. He jumped so high and he jumped so fast, his feet grew strong and his neck grew longer.

When Stretch saw that, he put the feed on top of the barrel. Big Boy jumped higher, stretched higher; and his feet, they grew stronger, and his neck grew longer.

So Stretch put the feed on top of a tub that stood on the barrel. Big Boy jumped higher and stretched his neck longer to get it, and his legs grew still stronger and his neck much longer.

Then Stretch put the grain on top o' two barrels. But that rooster got it there, too, and his neck and legs grew still stronger.

Big Boy was now tall as a steer and as strong. Stretch had an idea.

"If I kin git Big Boy strong as a horse, I'll need not buy a horse and won't bother my cows either."

So he kept raising the feed higher, and Big Boy kept on jumping and stretching till he was big 's a horse and just as strong.

Stretch harnessed Big Boy to a wagon, loaded it high with hay, and that rooster pulled it better than any horse on a Jersey farm.

"Hi, Big Boy! Soon you'll be good 's my shark-horse," and Stretch put him to work on the farm just as he would a thousand-pound percheron.

Big Boy plowed the land and harrowed it, too; drew loads of manure and mountain-high hay; pulled rocks from the fields and the family to church.

That rooster was famous from New Jersey to California, and Stretch was mighty proud of him. There was only one thing that bothered him.

Big Boy grew stronger all the time and ate more all the time.

One day Stretch had a fine idea. He added a little sand and cement to the feed. It was a good filler and carried weight, too.

Big Boy ate and never knew the difference.

The next day Stretch added a little more sand and cement, and Big Boy never knew the difference.

Feed was running high, and soon Stretch was feeding Big Boy more sand and cement than feed.

Came Christmastime when feed was highest. Stretch had lots of sand and lots of cement. So on Christmas day he used no feed at all, but mixed a big mess of sand and cement, put in things to make it look green and appetizing, and added a little corn likker to give it a flavor.

"That's a fine Christmas dinner for ye," Stretch cried to Big Boy.

Big Boy crowed so loud the barn shook on its beams, flapped his wings so the cows thought it was a hurricane, and jumped so high he near took the roof off. He was that excited. Then he set to eating.

It tasted good, it tasted warm, on that freezing cold day.

When he was done he laid down to sleep. The world was singing Christmas songs, and the concrete was churning inside o' Big Boy. The next morning the world outside was soft and white, and Big Boy was all concrete stone and hard, even to the wings and comb, but they had not lost their color.

Stretch was sorry for his loss, but he had other roosters, so he gave Big Boy as a present to the town to have him put on the firehouse.

On the firehouse he was put, and they set a siren in his bill with electric wires running to the fire chief's bed.

When the siren screamed in Big Boy's bill you could

hear it far and wide in Cumberland County. Volunteer firemen and citizens heard it and ran to the fire, and hens and roosters heard it and ran to Big Boy.

The fire was put out, but the hens and roosters couldn't be driven away from that concrete rooster no matter how hard folks tried.

Day and night the roosters crowed and the hens cackled, so that there was no peace in home or hearth.

In the end the mayor and the firemen and Stretch took down Big Boy just for the sake of peace.

He was put in the firehouse with the shinny red engines, and Stretch returned to his farm, performing wonders about which all Jersey has been talking to this very day.

Bees in the Bonnets in New Jersey

Kick the dust and raise the yeast,
Listen to the tale of a weddin' feast.

WENT to New Jersey to look for adventure, found enough for a bag full of holes.

Sun didn't shine black, rain didn't fall green, but on the reefs of the Passaic River lived Harry with his wife and nineteen children in a teeny weeny house. Twelve foot all around and not another inch.

"How can you live in such a teeny weeny house with such a large family, Harry?" said I.

"Happy and contented the whole day long. Good-by, I'm in a hurry."

"Hurry! Why?"

"Got t' go t' Forgetful Willie's wedlock frolic, him who is always forgettin' things."

Kick the dust and raise the yeast,
We're on our way to the weddin' feast.

Harry and his family twenty yards long went off, and so did I.

Heard a noise loud and screechy: Noisy Sall and Noisy Wall. Always quarrelin', always naggin'. Naggin' in the house, quarrelin' on the road; naggin' in the field, quarrelin' in the church; quarrelin' even while asleep.

"Always quarrelin', always naggin'. Give yourself and the state a rest," said I.

"Goin' to Foggy Willie's weddin', an' I say he'll be there."

"I say he won't," roared Wall. "He'll never remember his weddin' day."

"He will," screeched Sall.

"He won't," roared Wall.

They screeched and roared all the way, and you could hear them for near a mile.

> Kick the dust and raise the yeast,
> We're on our way to the weddin' feast.

Came to a house long and narrow, Len at one end, John at the other. Had between 'em more children than Harry but never lifted a finger to feed 'em.

Len and John were sittin' in the sun, their wives stood over 'em.

"Lazy hedgehogs, up from the dirt, y'll never get to Foggy Willie's wedlock frolic."

Len and John, they never moved, so their better halves, they yanked 'em up, put 'em on the road, to go to the wedlock frolic.

> Kick the dust and raise the yeast,
> I'm gettin' nearer to the weddin' feast.

Came a man, dressed like a beau, shouting on top o' his voice:

"I'm George Washington, look at the father of your country!"

"Where are you going, Sir?"

"Going to Forgetful Willie's wedding. But first I'll buy a six-cent drink and a good one-cent cigar."

Drank his drink, smoked his cigar, and went along the road.

> Kick the dust and raise the yeast,
> He's on his way to the weddin' feast.

Hove in sight Bill the cooper, with hair like a lion's mane. Roared like a lion, said he was one. Folks called 'm Bill the Roarer.

"Where are you goin', Bill the Roarer?"

"Goin' to roar at Foggy Willie's wedlock frolic."

He went his way and I went mine.

> Kick the dust an' raise the yeast,
> He's on his way to the weddin' feast.

Along the way came Jolly Jumpin' George with a hop an' a skip an' a jump.

"Why don't you walk as other folks do, Jolly Jumpin' George?"

"Want to be different from other folks. Folks find happiness in a hen's nest an' I find it wherever I go."

"Where are you goin', Jolly Jumpin' George?"

"Goin' to Foggy Willie's hitch-up frolic."

> Kick the dust an' raise the yeast,
> He's on his way to the weddin' feast.

Right behind him ran John the Noisy, shouting everything that was on his mind:

"I'm runnin' to the weddin' of Willie the Forgetful that's marryin' Katja with the pretty face." Off he was,

> Kickin' the dust an' raisin' the yeast,
> Shoutin' an' runnin' to the weddin' feast.

Came by slowly Rachel the singer, singin' a hymn sweet as a bird. She was on her way to the wedlock frolic to sing a hymn for the bride and groom.

> Kick the dust an' raise the yeast,
> She's on her way to the weddin' feast.

Down the road ran Cheap John. For a penny a month Cheap John worked for you, for me, for any, for all, and told the weather besides.

"Where are you running, Cheap John?" I said.

"Where all are runnin', there I'm runnin' too. Down to Clifton to the marryin' frolic."

> Kick the dust an' raise the yeast,
> I'm in Clifton town for the weddin' feast.

There was Katja the bride, sweet as a flower; there were her parents round and rosy; there were friends and relatives more than you could count—from all around Passaic County—but there wasn't any bridegroom there.

The dominie raised his eyebrows, the feast spread on

tables under the trees was getting cold, but Forgetful Willie had forgotten his wedding day!

> Kick the dust an' raise the yeast,
> They're waitin' for the weddin' feast.

"I told you so," cried Noisy Wall.

"Get that groom," folks cried loud.

"I'll get 'm quick," said Cheap John.

He ran like a partridge to the bridegroom's house and found him . . . hoeing his potato field!

Forgetful Willie, his mind all foggy, had forgotten his wedding day!

"Put on clean clothes quick 's thunder, bride an' guest are waitin' for y'."

Up leaped Willie, put on his good clothes quicker than he ever did before, and ran like a rabbit to his pretty bride.

Then Harry and his long family, Noisy Sall and Noisy Wall, Len and John and their goodwives, "George Washington" and Bill the Roarer, Jolly Jumpin' George and John the Noisy, Rachel the singer and Cheap John, groom and bride, parents, dominie, and friends, they all

> Kicked the dust and raised the yeast
> At Forgetful Willie's weddin' feast.

The Best Devil in the Land

THE nicest devil in all America is the Leeds Devil of New Jersey. His mother was Mistress Leeds, and this is how he came to the Garden State.

Mistress Leeds of Estelville had her full share of young ones. Fact is she had too many for one woman to tend, and one fine day there was another on the way.

She was full of ire and full of anger, and she cried, "I'd just as lief have a devil as a child."

The Devil was busy in Boston, but he heard it just the same and said with a grin, "Mistress Leeds, you'll have your wish."

The babe was born, and the moment it came into the world it changed at once into a little devil.

Its foot was cloven, there was a tail on its back. Its face was long like a collie dog and near as wide as a horse's head. And it had a pair of black wings on its back, besides. No devil in the land ever had that!

Before the mother and her friends could take a breath, that little Devil leaped on the window and flew away.

He went into the swamps in great Egg Harbor

and lived there, never harming bird or beast or man.

Folks just couldn't understand. He was not like the Devil of New England who was forever making trouble. He never did any harm and helped wherever he could.

Small wonder. His mother was a fine Christian, went to church on Sundays, and was respected by everyone.

Just the same, folks up and down South Jersey where that Devil roamed were mighty scared of 'm. All ran from him save one or two, and that made him very sad.

One day the good Leeds Devil was sitting at Great Egg Harbor River watching the waves running on the shore, thinking of his own sad, lonesome lot.

"Folks in New Jersey are just like these waves on the shore, rolling along restlessly without rhyme or reason, always banging their heads.

"Still, I'm their kind, and I feel sorry for 'em. There's a great war coming, with murdering and maiming that could be settled in a simple way. I'll go and warn 'em."

Off he rushed up and down and all around South Jersey, shouting and warning people not to go to war. He even went as far as Trenton, and he was in Woodstown, too. But wherever he went no one would listen to him. Said it was the Devil talking and fought the war just the same.

The goods Leeds Devil felt even sadder than before. He could not understand why folks would fight a war rather than listen to his warning.

Yet hope is everlasting, and so the good Leeds Devil always comes to Jersey to warn people of coming wars.

DELAWARE

The Blue-Hen
State

DELAWARE BAY

Herman and His Horse

IN THE long ago of our land there lived in little Delaware a man named Herman, who came from Bohemia in Europe. When Herman saw the Blue State and how beautiful it was, rich with oak, hickory, and pine, he said, "Now I never want to go back to Bohemia."

So he built himself a castle in the new land, tilled the soil, and drew maps of the wilderness. And one of his greatest pleasures was to raise and run fine horses.

One day he had to go to New Amsterdam, so he said to his overseer, "Saddle me my finest horse, I'm off to New Amsterdam to see about some good land I own there and perhaps visit Governor Stuyvesant with the silver peg-leg and the evil temper."

Herman's finest horse, saddled and shod, was brought, and he rode to New Amsterdam town, where the fiery peg-leg governor ruled with an iron hand.

Now, I must tell you that the governor with the single leg had a great grudge against Herman. He said that Herman made a map for Lord Baltimore of Maryland which gave the English a tract of land that belonged rightfully to the Dutch, and, if ever he laid his hands on him, he'd punish him for this.

When he learned that Herman had come to the city
by the sea, he rubbed his hands and cried he'd finish that
vile fellow who favored the English over the Dutch.

The governor ordered soldiers to arrest the Dela-
warean and lock him in the big warehouse, where there
was little chance for escape.

Twelve armed men were sent out, and soon they had
Herman from Delaware under lock and key in the warehouse.

It took weeks before there was a trial, at which Herman had no right to defend himself. In the end he was
sentenced by the hard governor to be executed for trea-
son against New Amsterdam for making a false map
favoring Lord Baltimore with land that rightfully belonged to the Dutch. In vain Herman argued and
stormed. He was far from friends, and none would help
him.

The day for the execution was set, and Master Herman
thought deep and thought hard of some way to escape,
for he was nowhere near ready to die. Life in Delaware
was too pleasant.

He thought all day when carts rumbled by and thought
all night when stars shone in the sky, and in the end the
good Lord gave him a good thought, a fearless one, and
one befitting him.

He would be saved by his horse.

When the jailer brought him food the next day he saw
a strange sight. Herman was standing in the center of the

room gibbering and jabbering words that had in them neither sense nor reason.

The jailer gaped, then he asked what was wrong, but he could not get a word of sense out of the prisoner.

Soon all knew that Herman of Delaware had lost his mind.

Day after day this went on, with the prisoner always gibbering. Just a few words could be made out, words that were piteous pleas to see his horse once more before he died.

One day he even fell on his knees before his jailer, pleading to let him see his horse one more time before he died. The jailer promised to bring the horse the next day. And bring it he did the next morning.

It was not hard to lead the animal right into the chamber where Herman was. Broad steps of stone led up to an entrance wide enough to let in a team of horses and a wagon. The chamber proper was very large and high for keeping bales of grain, and on one side there was a wide window looking down toward the Hudson River.

Master Herman was fully dressed when the jailer opened the door to let the horse come in.

Master and horse greeted each other, and then Herman mounted the steed and rode him around the chamber again and again, talking to it softly, sweetly, and stroking its mane.

Of a sudden he bent low, stiffened his boots, and whispered something in its ears. The horse seemed to understand. With one lithe leap it was through the window and on the ground. The jailer thought the two were surely killed, for the leap down was full fifteen feet. But the horse just kept on running, while the bystanders were too surprised to move hand or foot. By then horse and rider were past houses in the clear land, riding like lightning toward the river. In they plunged, and before the surprised Dutchmen were a-horse, Herman was near across the river and on the Jersey side.

Then began a race between Herman and the Dutchmen of which folk tell to this very day.

They raced through swamps and woods, through fields and streams, Herman in the fore, the Dutchmen far behind. So they came to New Jersey land and reached the noble Delaware, right opposite New Castle town. There the horse swam across until it came to Herman's castle, and master and animal were safe.

And in Delaware there were feasts and rejoicing to celebrate the feat of the great hero.

The Fiddler
of Fiddler's Bridge

THERE'S heaps o' good stories about black folks, an' heaps o' good stories about white folks, but there is a good story I heard tell about black folks an' white folks at one an' the same time. It's a story I heard from a black man down in Saint Georges in Delaware.

It's the story about the fiddler man who got born in a cabin standin' right in the middle o' seven swamp maples off Scot's run.

From the day that boy could toddle or just say Mammy or Pappy he was forever singin' an' playin' with sticks, beatin' 'gainst tree bark makin' sounds like a drum.

That fiddler boy's parents had come straight from Afriky chained in iron on a dirty slave ship, but when their little son was born they were so glad, they didn't think no more 'bout the chains or the land from which they come.

Folks called that boy Jacob, an' when he grew up he had to work like his Pappy an' Mammy. But he'd quicker play on the fiddle he made from a box, with a bow he made from a branch, than do any kind o' work.

One day he saved enough money to buy him a regular fiddle, an' from then on Jacob wouldn't change his lot with an angel on high or Massa Osborn livin' in the big house.

He was always playin' tunes he heard from people an' tunes he heard in his head. He'd be playin' when he should've been workin', an' folks said Jacob was no good with a hoe in his hand but fine with a fiddle under his chin.

There was one man thought Jacob was no good no-how, an' that was the evil-eyed overseer who was takin' care o' the farm. Even when Jacob was asked to frolics an' dances, the overseer would growl. Said folks shouldn't favor that good-for-nothin' lazy rascal.

Just the same, there was no dance or frolic to which Jacob wasn't asked, an' that made the evil-eyed overseer mighty mad.

One day Jacob heard the low voice of freedom talk, so he began fiddlin' the freedom song right in the middle o' the day when the evil-eyed overseer stood not far from him.

It made that mean fellow mad as a black cat out for trouble. He went up to Jacob an' began lashin' him. He lashed him so long, poor Jacob fell to the ground an' lay still for a long time.

When he got up he was kind o' different from before. He wouldn't talk reg'lar to nobody an' he wouldn't work no matter how much the overseer whipped him. 'Stead o' that he was singin' an' playin' his fiddle all day, an' all night, too. No 'mount o' talk or whippin' could make him work. An' the playin' an' singin' was different from before. 'Twas tunes he remembered his mother sang when he was a little pickaninny.

Them songs troubled black folks an' white folks, too. They began sayin' Jacob was touched in the head, or maybe conjured.

No one bothered him from then on, not even the evil-eyed overseer. He let Jacob run his way, he was that scared.

Folks didn't ask him much to frolics, either, for it's best not to have a conjure man 'cept when you need 'm for sickness or love.

Jacob went his way singin' freedom songs or Afriky songs an' fiddlin' sweet tunes, and the fiddlin' was so sweet, folks said the Devil himself was swingin' that bow.

Jacob lived by himself in a little hut near an old bridge. There were three swamp willows on one side o' that bridge an' four swamp willows on the other, an' their branches were wild like a woman's hair that's not combed in the mornin'. Jacob slept in the hut an' fiddled on the bridge when swamp owls were cryin'. So folks began callin' it Fiddler's Bridge.

All day long he played tunes to the fish shootin' 'round the water an' to the yellow an' gray snappin' turtles blinkin' their little eyes. He sat there most o' the night, too, playin' to the croakin' frogs an' the cryin' whip-poorwills.

When young folks or old, black or white, passed by goin' to Red Lion or Dragon Creek, or Black Bird or

Smyrna, they'd make sport o' poor old Jacob an' call him the crazy fiddler fiddlin' on Fiddler's Bridge.

Jacob, he never minded talk. He listened to his own music or to the wind playin' in the swamp willows, to the singin' water an' the birds. Or maybe he'd watch the tree-shadow folk runnin' in the water. They was his friends an' never made sport o' him or called him names. They was callin' him instead to come live with 'em.

One fine night when the yellow moon was lazy-like on the trees, seemed all the frogs in the state o' Delaware an' all the whippoorwills an' katydids an' swamp owls came to listen to Jacob fiddlin' on Fiddler's Bridge.

There was great singin' in the water under the bridge, too, callin' mor'n it ever did for 'm to come an' live there so he'd never have trouble from the evil-eyed overseer or from mockin' folks.

So Jacob jest slid down the cool, singin' water, his fiddle under his chin an' his bow in his hand . . . to be playin' for friends only.

Folks all around said crazy Jacob had drowned himself when he was in a crazy fit. But you an' I know better.

One night a gay company comin' from a tavern passed over the bridge, an' one of 'em said just for devilment:

"Let's throw some silver in the river for crazy Jacob to play."

They threw in the coins, an' quick come from the water the sweetest music y' ever heard. Y' just could have knocked them young uns over with a blade o' grass.

They ran away, tellin' everybody, black an' white,

'bout it. From then on, when folks walked over that bridge on a moony midnight an' threw in a coin, there'd be playin' to melt the heart and set feet a-dancin'.

Some didn't believe this an' said it was just talk of ignorant folks who didn't know no better.

One night Massa Osborn, the rich man in the big house nearby, made a great big party for quality folks an' friends from all round. Everybody was there dressed in fine clothes havin' a great time.

Massa Osborn thought he'd have some fun, so he called an ol' black fiddlin' man, gave him money, an' told 'm to hide behind the swamp willows on Fiddler's Bridge so's none 'd see 'm, an' when he heard silver coins droppin' over the bridge he should play the tunes he knew.

That ol' black man knew the best way to git along with white folks is to say yes, so he said he'd do it.

Well, there was dancin' in Massa Osborn's house, an' then Massa Osborn told the company the story 'bout Fiddler's Bridge an' asked 'em to go on it an' try their luck. Maybe if they'd drop some silver coins over the bridge at midnight Jacob 'd play a tune for 'em.

All the company ran to Fiddler's Bridge, for they thought it 'd be good sport to hear a ghost playin'.

The moon was shinin' high, the wind was makin' music over the water an' through them swamp trees, while the white folks was throwin' silver coins over the bridge.

Then there was heard such sweet playin' as was never heard from that runnin' water. The fine company was mighty pleased, an' back to the big house they went, marvelin' at the fiddlin' ghost.

Then Massa Osborn told 'em 'twas no ghost at all but a livin' black man hidin' behind the trees playin' as he was told to do when he saw the company throwin' coins over the bridge.

But that ain't what I heard tell. I heard tell that livin' black fiddlin' man said he'd have no business foolin' with ghosts for any man, even for Massa Osborn, the richest man in Delaware. 'Stead o' goin' on Fiddler's Bridge, he'd gone home to his cabin. He never raised his bow to play any fiddle that night. The playin' folks heard on the bridge was really done by Jacob, deep under the water. That's what my grandmammy tol' me. An' there's no contradictin' this, for she heard it with her own ears, jest as you're hearin' it with yours.

Fiery-Tempered Jake

DOWN in Delaware folks tell about Fiery-Tempered Jake, who did what few men ever did. He won a fair maid, young Kezia, when everyone tried to stop him; got the best of her when she crossed him; and beat the Devil at his own game.

Pert Kezia was pretty as a daisy and chipper as a robin. Her cheeks were pink and blooming, her eyes were bright and dancing, and her hair was soft and brown. She turned the head of every young fellow at Ferris Corner, and so her mother sent her off to another farm to keep her out of mischief and to keep the men at work. But there she met young Jake, tall as a cedar, a temper like the wind, and a thinking head. It didn't take long until Jake and Kezia thought of each other all day long and spoke to each other all evening long. Pretty soon they found they couldn't live without each other, and so one fine morning without saying a word to friend or foe Jake mounted his fine dapple steed, put Kezia on the pillion behind him, and rode to New Castle town for to be married by a man of God. Maybe it was right or maybe it was wrong, but what's right for one may be wrong for another, and only the Lord can tell that.

132

Kezia's parents were angry, but Jake's parents were glad and gave them a house and farm, where they lived in happiness and arguments.

Came along the Revolution, when men and boys fought for liberty and freedom, and Jake was among the foremost of his state to volunteer and soon became a leader.

One day he had to go to Philadelphia to meet men from other towns to make a grave decision.

Now, Kezia had some tea bought months before the war. She was a true and patriotic American and would not buy tea after that from the British at any price, but she saw no harm in drinking what she had bought long before the war.

When her husband went to Philadelphia she asked a few gossips living nearby for an afternoon's visit and some tea as well.

It was a lovely day, and Kezia's friends came as they were bid. There was talk and laughter while the kettle was on the fire bubbling and dancing in chorus.

But alas for the merry dames! Jake missed the ferry at Christene and had to return to go the next morning. So he went back through woods and streams and paths until he reached his own good farm and home.

He put up the horse and walked to the house, from which came great chatter and laughter, as you might expect when women get together. They made so much noise they never heard the opening of the door.

Jake took just one glance at the bubbling kettle and

smelled the fragrance of "English" tea, which every true
American had sworn not to drink! It raised Jake's fiery
temper as nothing had before.

In one leap he was at the stove, lifted the boiling brass
kettle, and threw it fiercely through the open door among
the hens picking at the grass.

Kezia turned mad as a fighting Indian. She screamed
and cried, "How dare you do such a thing? 'Tis not fit
for a gentleman. You're a beast and should hide your
head in shame. You're a cruel bully just because you're
stronger."

She kept this up while the women cried the same in
chorus.

That was just too much for Jake. He picked up his
wife, who was small, and tossed her clean out-of-doors
after the teapot and ordered the women to leave his house.
Out they rushed, and he slammed the door behind them.

As for Kezia, she picked herself up none the worse
for the fall and ran from window to door, shouting,
"You're the worst bully that ever was! You've the Devil's
temper, and some day he'll carry you off to keep him
company!"

For days after she would not speak to him, but when
the time came for him to go with other Delaware men
to fight for home and land they kissed good-by.

The war was over, and the years went by. One fine
day Jake returned with his regiment without a scratch
or hurt even to his temper. That had grown worse with

the years. All friends who fought by his side agreed he had the Devil's own temper.

The Devil with his little horns and long tail, who was then in Massachusetts, heard it and thought he would find out for himself if this were so. If it were, he could claim Jake as a partner.

It was an autumn day in Delaware that brings a song to the heart. The wind played in the white oaks and yellow poplars, and bees drank nectar in the shining flowers. But Kezia and Jake had a silly argument, the kind married folks often have, and Jake began to rant and roar, as was ever his wont, so you could hear him clear to Massachusetts, and there the Devil heard him.

With three leaps he was in Ferris Corner in Jake's peach orchard, where the two were arguing about when peaches should be gathered.

Jake was roaring on the top of his voice, and Kezia was screaming and then ran into the house.

No sooner had she disappeared than the Devil in a long, black surcoat and swishing tail stood before the open-mouthed Jake, bowing low.

"Master Jake," said the Devil with a voice smooth as slithering hot oil, "I heard about your fiery temper all the way to Massachusetts, and I came to find out if it were really so. It is indeed, even better than I thought. It is fully as evil as mine, and I'll be pleased to take you as my partner. If I find you twice again in such roaring anger you'll be mine. I'll watch you. Good-by."

This sobered Jake more than I can tell you. He crossed

himself three times and said his daily prayer—a thing he hadn't done for a very long time. Then, pale and silent, he came into the house.

Kezia saw the change and asked the reason, but Jake would not tell.

From that day on he was a different man, and he never lost his temper. He joined the church and freed the slaves. He even forbade his daughters to wear flowers or to dance. But both, being daughters of Kezia, did these things just the same. And it never did them any harm.

Do you think Jake lost his temper? Never! Not even a single time, for he remembered that the Devil was watching all the time. He figured 'twas better to be a forgiving father than a partner of the Devil.

> I think so, too,
> And so do you.
>
> The house is there,
> So's the kettle bright.
> The story's fair,
> The lesson's right.

The Enemy in the Night

IN THE olden days, in the golden days, when settlers first came to rich, big America, there was a great rivalry between the Dutch, who came from Holland and settled on Manhattan by the sea, and the Swedes, who came from Sweden and settled on the Delaware that runs into Delaware Bay.

The Dutch looked with greedy eyes on the rich, level lands and the soft hills covered with tall pines and oak. But the biggest eyes of all had "Peg-leg" Governor Stuyvesant of New Amsterdam. He stomped about on his silver-pegged, wooden leg trying to frighten men in towns and beasts in the forests. He ranted and cried, "If we take Fort Christina and Fort Casimir, all the land of the Swedes will be ours."

The Swedes knew this well and were ever on the lookout. One day Governor Stuyvesant decided to make his boasting good. He sent some spies disguised as traders to Fort Christina to learn how strong the enemy was.

Now, the spies came right when a boatload of settlers and soldiers from the homeland arrived at the fort. There was rejoicing at the little settlement, with singing and feasting to greet the newcomers. The spies saw this, as well as little wooden log cabins and rich pelts traded with the Indians and a-plenty of other goods of the world.

The new soldiers were glad to see all these riches, as well as the square fort with its cannon and wooden stockade. But when they looked into the forests and marshes full of croaking frogs and rotting stumps shaped like bearded wizards, fear crept into their hearts.

Folks said the marshes and woods were full of lions and large grim dragons and rattlesnakes with jaws like dogs.

But soldiers must do their tasks, be they afeared or not. So they worked on duty, and off as well, until they forgot their fears of the silent forests and noisy marshes.

But the spies watched all the time.

One night in the lovely month of June, Sved, one of the new Swedish soldiers, was on watch. The starlit night was filled with singing little insects and croaking of the frogs in the marshes.

Sved, his iron helmet on his head to keep off the insects buzzing around him, was walking from one corner to the other of the square stockade.

He stared into the black from which came the noises like waves of the sea. Never had he heard such noises before. His legs felt weak in his wide boots, and the gun on his shoulder shook.

A big yellow moon crept up behind the black trees, and the stars shone sharp on stumps and grass and log house. The shadows moved like bewitched birds and beasts with giant claws and long beaks.

Sved was sure he saw lions with snaky tails and dragons with burning eyes crawling on the ground. He wished he had never come to this land, full of wizards and witches to frighten even a man with a blunderbuss.

Of a sudden a strange light leaped up in the grasses near the woods! Another shot through the dark marsh! Another! And another!

Sved stood stone still. He turned pale in his face and heart as well.

Maybe it was the Dutch from New Amsterdam led by fierce "Peg-leg" Stuyvesant, of whom he had heard so many dire tales. His mouth was so dry he could not shout.

There! More of the bewitched lights! More and more of them! On all sides! Leaping about and coming nearer!

Maybe it was painted Indians, who skinned the faces of prisoners and cut off fingers and toes and danced round and round with yelling glee! They often brandished torches while attacking!

And the bellowing of bullfrogs in the marshes! It might be shooting, it was so loud! And the crinking cries of tree toads and wild screeches of birds! Indians on the war-path screeched and yelled!

Now the tapers were everywhere, all around, moving, flying in all directions! Thousands of them! They were the fierce Dutchmen and the wild Indians attacking Fort Christina!

Sved's tongue now loosened and he began shouting, "Alarm! Alarm! The enemy is about!"

The drummer beat his drum, and soldiers and Lieutenant Elias rushed up with muskets ready for defense. Settlers came running from their log houses; women and children cried with fear.

"Where is the enemy!"

"The enemy is here close to the fort; they carry burning tapers to burn the houses," bellowed Sved. He was no longer afeared, seeing so many people about him.

His outstretched hand pointed to the lights in woods and fields and marsh coming up and dying off as they often do in the high summer months in the country. They were bright Spanish flies or fireflies playing their nightly game in pleasure for themselves and others as well.

First the colonists and soldiers were in great anger, but then they laughed at stupid Sved, who took innocent Spanish flies for the enemy.

The tale spread far and wide, and the spies brought it to "Peg-leg" Peter Stuyvesant sitting like a spider in New Amsterdam.

"If all the Swedes in Fort Christina are so silly, they'll be easy game," he cried.

He manned his ship, set sail, and conquered Fort Christina without hurting man or beast. Which is the finest way of all to end a war! He never thought perhaps the Swedes were too smart to fight.

That's what old people tell around Fort Christina right in Wilmington in the Diamond State of Delaware.

Dutch Peter and the Fortunetelling Tailor

THERE lived a man in Wilmington who wasn't liked by anyone. He was a Hessian soldier who deserted the English army after fighting with them at Brandywine against American freedom. People called him Dutch Peter, and he was sexton of the Trinity Church.

No one liked that Hessian soldier, but least of all Mistress Russel, who sold vegetables, and Master Fredrick the tailor man, who could tell fortunes and make gold-finding rods.

Mistress Russel came every Wednesday and Saturday to the marketplace with her little wooden cart drawn by her good cow Piedy and followed by her little dog no bigger than a growing chick of a blue hen of Delaware. It was as nice a dog as you ever saw, and Mistress Russel said so.

Everybody agreed with her save that Hessian soldier, who drove the dog away and even kicked it when it followed Mistress Russel to the church. That's why Mistress Russel couldn't stand the sight of that soldier.

Master Fredrick did not like the Hessian for a very good reason, too. He was forever darkening the tailor's door a-talking to Master Fredrick's wife, Dutch Dolly, and always bothering the tailor to give him a gold-finding rod to make him a rich man without doing any work.

One sweet Sunday morning Mistress Russel went to Trinity Church a-riding on her wooden wagon pulled by Piedy the good cow, and alongside ran her little dog. She stopped near the church, where all the horses and carts were standing, and tied up Piedy. Then she gave her a little hay and went to the church, a stick in one hand, her prayer book in the other, followed by her little dog.

At the door stood Dutch Peter, fat and growling, an evil look in his eyes. No sooner did he spy Mistress Russel than he bellowed, "You don't come mit dat dok here, God be tankful and tings, I tell you."

Mistress Russel just kept on walking, swinging her stick, and not in the least afeared. But when she came to the church door, Dutch Peter raised his heavy-booted foot and gave the little dog a fierce kick, which set the poor thing yelping and running. At that Mistress Russel raised her stick and rained blows with all her might on cruel Dutch Peter's back.

Burgesses, deacons, merchant men, farmers, and their wives ran up, and soon there was peace, and Mistress Russel went into the church followed by her limping little dog.

That very evening good Mistress Russel went to Master Fredrick, the fortunetelling tailor, who lived on King and Hanover streets.

The door was open, and by the light of the moon she saw the tailor sitting crosswise on the table right near the window.

Above his head hung a bag of onions, and next to him were a loaf of bread and a cup of salt. Since it was God's day he was not working at all, just looking through the window at the bright stars to learn the fortune of the good people in Wilmington in Delaware.

"Good evening to you, Master Fredrick, where's your goodwife, Mistress Dolly? I missed her yesterday with her fine vegetables. You know she always sits beside me in the marketplace."

"Good evenin', Mistress Russel," Fredrick replied, "my wife Dolly's gone to Dover a-visitin'. She'll not return till late tomorrow eve."

"I'm glad to hear this, Master Fredrick, for my errand is the kind your wife doesn't like overmuch. 'Tis well known she does not favor your fortunetelling and selling charms, and I want a charm to punish a mean fellow 'd even hurt a poor little dog. You know well of whom I'm speaking, for you were to church and saw how cruelly he hurt my poor little dog."

"Dutch Peter's a mean and a brutal lout who is forever running to my house gabbing with Mistress Dolly enough to fill the town and botherin' me for gold-finding rods. If I had my way I'd have a rod a-dancin' on his back."

"Ah, Master, how I wish for the old whipping post we

once had in our town, and he tied to it, and me to do the whipping! That's what should be done to a fellow that kicks a poor little dog for no reason at all. But there was a good stick a-dancing on his back on Sunday. Now I want you to give me a charm so that brutish lout can never kick my dog again."

For a time the fortunetelling tailor looked into the starry sky. Then there came a broad smile on his wrinkled face.

He was a kindly man telling fortunes by the stars and trying to help people wherever he could. But he also loved a good joke and had nothing against playing one if it did no harm. Said he to Mistress Russel:

"Mistress, I say again, Dutch Peter is a mean man an' cruel. It tells in the stars he'll be punished an' never hurt yer dog again, for he'll be no sexton in our church, if ye help with somethin' I've in mind."

"That I gladly will, with all that's in my power," said she.

"Mistress Russel, Dutch Peter'll be here soon. He comes every Sunday eve to gossip with my wife an' to bother me for gold-findin' rods. I've just thought of a way that 'll stop 'm from comin' here an' hurtin' your dog—if ye'll help me. An' this is my plan, mistress. When he comes here with his fat black-powder face, gossipin' in language no man can figure out, all ye have to do is just stand behind that door a-groanin' an' saying over an' over an' over again in a moanin' voice: 'Sexton, leave that church! Sexton, leave that church!' Do that each time ye hear me cough. I know that'll frighten him so he'll run away even farther than he ran from the English."

"That's simple."

"An' if ye want, mistress, ye can also take a sheet an' wind it around ye an' come in when ye hear me kind o' sneezin'. Then he'll surely run quicker'n a mouse in sight of a cat."

Mistress Russel thought this was a grand idea. There was a big smile on her thin, drawn face, on which there rarely was a smile, and she said she'd surely do it.

The big yellow moon like a shiny waxy cheese moved in the sky, and there were footsteps coming down King Street.

"That's his walk, I know it for certain," said Fredrick. "Now, go ye behind that door leadin' in the other room and do as I've told ye. Remember, ye'll find a sheet in the chest that's in there."

Mistress Russel went in the other chamber. Soon Dutch Peter, big and fat, came in. His face was nearly all black from black powder that once blew into it when he was blasting rock.

"Goot evening, Master Fredrick, where is Mistress Tolly?" said he.

"Good evening, Master Peter, she's gone to Dover visitin' an' won't be back till tomorrow," replied Fredrick.

"Ah, then we can have a little *klatch*," and he plumped himself in a chair. "Now we're alone, Master Fredrick, and I want to speak to you. You can tell fortunes by the stars, and you can make golt-finding rods, so you can make me a golt-finding rod. I'll pay you goot money for it—when I find a treasure like Captain Kitt's or another pirate's. Come, I'm your goot friend and tings."

He kept on begging, while Fredrick looked at the black-blue sky where the stars shone so bright they seemed to be moving. Then the tailor said, "Master Peter, the stars favor ye tonight, an' I think I can give ye a gold-findin' rod but. . . ."

"Dat's goot, dat's fine!" Dutch Peter broke in.

". . . but," continued Fredrick, "there's a black shadow standin' in the way. There's an evil spirit workin' against ye."

"Vy, Vy?"

"Who knows?" said Fredrick. "There's a battle o' spirits goin' on for ye this very minute in the spheres o' the world."

"About me?" said Peter, much surprised.

"About ye. These evil forces an' the good forces are battlin' whether ye're to get the gold-findin' rod. D'ye hear 'm?"

"I don't hear noting, only frogs and whippoorwills."

"That's it, the whippoorwills! That's a bad omen. Ye know, whippoorwills are souls o' people who didn't finish their work in this world, so they go around cryin', wantin' to finish it. That's bad. I fear yer good spirits aren't strong enough. Let's hope an' pray." And then he coughed a little.

At that there was a moaning from behind the door and

a voice saying, "Sexton, leave that church! Sexton, leave that church! Sexton, leave that church!"

Peter turned pale and sick and cried, "What's dat, Master Fredrick?"

"Dutch Peter," Fredrick said solemnly, "that's the spirits tellin' ye what ye must do. Yer evil spirits are stronger," and he coughed a little.

Again there was a moaning voice and a crying, "Sexton, leave that church! Sexton, leave that church! Sexton, leave that church!"

"Vat shall I do, Master Fredrick?" Dutch Peter's teeth were chattering, and he looked green in the moonlight. "Please help me!"

Then Fredrick sneezed, and the door opened and there stood a ghost dressed in a white sheet crying shrilly, "Sexton, leave that church!"

"Run, Peter," cried Fredrick. "Run an' leave the church as ye're ordered to!"

Dutch Peter bolted through the door faster than he'd ever run, leaving Fredrick and Mistress Russel behind.

They laughed till the tears ran down their cheeks.

The very next day Dutch Peter left the church and would no more be sexton.

From then on Mistress Russel went to church with her little dog no bigger than a chick of a blue hen of Delaware, and no one ever bothered her.

Fearless John and the Giant Monster

YOU may speak of smart and fearless men that lived in Delaware, but never a one was more fearless than Ol' John. That's what Ol' John said.

Ol' John never did more work than he had to. And the most he did was sit at the toll bridge a little way from the railroad right in Wilmington, collecting fares from anyone who wanted to go over the bridge of the river. And wasn't he smart at collecting!

One day Master Vandevere, who owned the toll bridge, said to him, "Ol' John, the governor and his staff are coming over the bridge to my house. He's a friend of mine, and don't you ask him for any toll."

"I sure won't, Master Vandevere," said Ol' John.

The sun was high and the wind blew warm when the governor and his lieutenants all dressed in fine clothes came to the bridge. Ol' John looked more important than a rooster crowing in the early morn. He spoke loud for all to hear without hesitation or fear, "Y'ain't all governors, are ye?"

"No, just one of us," said one of the gentlemen, smiling, who was the governor.

"Then only one o' ye goes free over the bridge, the rest's got t' pay."

And pay they did, not minding it for the laugh they had.

But the smartest thing and most courageous Ol' John ever did, so it is remembered by good Delawareans to this day, is when he fought fearlessly the great battle with the awful monster in a canoe, and this is how it happened.

In the fall of the season, when the leaves turned fiery red, John and Andrew, the young sons of Master Vandevere, and some of their friends, French refugees from San Domingo, went shooting ducks in the marshes of New Jersey, where the marshes are more marshy than in Delaware.

The gay company took their boat right into the bay and rowed across to the Jersey shore. There they had a great time visiting friends and shooting to their hearts' content.

In the evening they had as much as their boat could carry, and perhaps a little more, for their friend had put in the largest pumpkin in all New Jersey as a special gift. It was near half as big as a calf or maybe bigger.

"For," said the man who grew the pumpkin, "wild ducks taste better than any meat if followed by a fine pumpkin pie, and I know Mistress Vandevere can bake as fine a pie as any woman in the land. We want to show her the kind of pumpkin that grows up New Jersey way."

They rowed across, singing songs, and came up the Brandywine River, landing at the toll bridge near where the manor house stood. They tied the boat to a post, went up to the house, and on the way they met Ol' John.

"Ol' John," cried Andrew, "do you think you're strong enough to bring in what we brought in the boat?"

"I'm strong enough, Master Andrew, to carry anything ye shot today unless it's the biggest bear or buck ever seen hereabouts. An' maybe I could bring in the bear or buck as well. I'll fetch what's in the boat, and I need no help from you young fellers either."

Off he went through the black night. He knew the way blindfolded.

Ol' John plodded through shrubs and ferns till he felt the boat. Then he jumped in with his heavy boots to pick up the game that was there.

No sooner did his heavy boots hit the wood than the boat bent upward from his weight, and a terrible, strange thing happened! A great big monster without legs and arms shot forward and threw him down with a mighty blow.

Now, John had never battled with a monster without arms and legs. He bellowed like a bull, barked like a dog, and leaped out of the boat, spun twice around, and ran for all he was worth. But soon he stopped, remembering only cowards ran from danger. He went back cautiously, picking up a big rock and a heavy stick for protection. He waited for a time, staring into the dark. There was no sound save the soft lapping of the water against the sides of the boat. The monster was gone!

He stepped carefully into the boat. No sooner was he in with one foot than once again the boat leaped up in the air, and again the legless, armless monster hit him with the force of a five-hundred-pound bear, knocking him in the water!

Up John leaped, screaming like a wildcat, "Help! Murder! To the rescue!"

He screamed so loud that those in the big house heard him and rushed out to see what the ruckus was about.

John had come running up the path and met men and women running pell-mell: friends, guests, sons, daughters, even to young Rachel who could hardly walk. They were armed with guns and hatchets, sticks and stones; many carried lanterns, shouting, "What is it? What is it?"

"There's a wild monster in the boat! He ain't got no arms nor legs, an' every time I put my foot in that boat he knocks me down. He weighs near five hundred pounds an' never opens his mouth, just strikes like thunder. It's a terrible monster!"

Everyone now rushed to the bridge where the boat was moored, Ol' John leading. The nearer they got, the more cautiously they walked. Lanterns were raised high, and eyes peered in the dark.

Right then and there there was a rift in the clouds, and a soft silver moon shed its light all around. It showed the trees, the bridge, the river, and the boat, one end full of wild ducks, and in front of them, about the middle—a round, yellow, giant pumpkin with a thick green knob at one end. . . .

Every time Ol' John had stepped into the boat the pumpkin had rolled forward and hit him hard. That was the monster!

For a minute there was a silence, then the laughter broke loose—at the monster! And at fearless Ol' John!

John looked silly, grumbled about darkness and silly fools letting a rolling thing like that in the boat, then went off. The company returned, laughing and telling over and over again the battle of Fearless John with the giant pumpkin.

The Ghost
of Samuel Chew

IN THE days that are passed, there lived in Dover, in Delaware, a chief justice called Samuel Chew. He was a strict man and just, but all these virtues did not prevent the people of the town from making sport of his name now and then. Some would sneeze and say it was to the good health of the chief justice; culprits would move their jaws up and down as 'tis done in chewing and tearing and say: thus and so it happens when Chief Justice Chew sits in court with his big white wig. The judge did not like this, and he often rebuked the mockers. As for wrong-doers, he punished them properly for their crimes. So he led an upright life, loved by those who were honest and feared by those who did evil.

The years went by, and the good, stern judge grew older, and one day when he had reached a ripe age he went to where there is but one Judge sitting on a throne of gold with angels all around Him.

There was a fine funeral from the red-brick house where the justice lived, and a seemly service in church.

Thenafter men sneezed aloud or moved their jaws, grinding and chewing without fear or fine.

But they reckoned without their ghost. Little did they dream that the spirit of the chief justice was still on earth listening to every sneeze and hearing every chew done in offense of his good name.

In truth he was hurt. His anger was aroused by the lack of respect shown to him by the people of Dover. And so he decided he'd put a stop to it.

One night when it was dark and the wild wind wailed, he came forth in search of those who mocked him.

A black shroud around him and a white wig on his head, he floated through the streets of Dover until he came to the old poplar tree, which he loved for its strength and straightness. There he stood, watching men who came from taverns and women who went to gossip, to see if anyone sneezed or chewed or spoke of him without proper respect.

The old poplar's leaves waved above him while he waved silently to and fro under them.

Came along one, David, a farmer, on his way to the tavern to have a little talk with friends of Old England and drink a hot drink to drive away the cold of the night. He was hatless, and the sharp wind tried to tear the hair from his head.

David walked as fast as he could, for his head was cold and he was sneezing all the time.

The good ghost, seeing him come and sneezing all the time, thought the countryman was making sport of him.

He raised his face full to the moon so you could see it white and ghostly, with wide, staring eyes.

Poor David, who would not harm a cricket, was frightened near death, for he knew the justice well and remembered certain harsh sentences given to those who deserved them. He raised a great howl and ran home swifter than a deer running from a pack of dogs.

He told his terrible adventure to his wife and children, and all hardly slept a wink. In the morning they told it to a neighbor, and soon the news of David's terrible adventure with the ghost of Justice Samuel Chew spread far and wide.

Now, some believed it and some did not, and those who did not kachewed and ground their teeth just to show those who believed how little they were afeared of the ghost David said he had seen.

So a little time passed, and men forgot the ghost until one night when Peter, the miller of Dover town, was walking home from the tavern.

Again it was a stormy night with rain coming down and the wind howling company. The kind of night fit for ghosts, good and bad. Peter held a lighted lantern in his hand that swung with every gust of wind. Of a sudden there came a blast that flung the lantern from his hand. He was then before the poplar tree and, lifting his eyes to look around for his lost lantern, saw . . . the ghost of Chief Justice Chew staring with angry eyes at him and pointing an accusing finger at him. For you must know our miller was guilty now and then of taking some flour for himself which rightly did not belong to him.

Peter was no greater a hero than David. He turned whiter than his flour and set up a great fierce cry of Murder! Lord!, and ran quicker than a frightened hare straight to his home. For a time he could not speak. His teeth chattered, and he kept on gibbering about ghosts and Chew, but after a time he told of the apparition he had seen. In a short time all the town knew the tale, and a great fear fell upon the good citizens of Dover town.

Everyone was now afeared to put a foot out-o'-doors as soon as the sun had set. Little children hid behind their mothers' skirts, and 'twas said the dogs howled mournfully all night long.

All were afeared of the ghost of Samuel Chew that was abroad, watching for every man to keep his peace and do nothing to anger him.

Not a one was without a little guilt somewhere in life of which no man knew of but which a ghost 'd surely know.

At night the roads were shunned like the very plague. Taverns were lighted as always, but deserted. Each man kept to his home, glum and silent instead of arguing about the latest politics or gossip.

Affairs of towns and settlement were no more discussed along with porter and sweet cider. Truly it was a sad state of affairs in Dover, and all the men, women, and children suffered from it.

But the greatest sufferers of all were the tavernkeepers,

who sat all night with long faces around their gleaming fireplaces.

So matters went for quite a time till one day Mistress Cook, who owned a fine and respectable tavern, had a good thought.

She called a meeting of all the shopkeepers and tavern-keepers and said to them:

"Friends, we want the good people of our town to come to our shops and taverns, and the good people of our town want the same. But since the ghost of our late and lamented Chief Justice Chew appears under the poplar tree, no man or woman has visited us, and there is anger and gloom everywhere. Something must be done about it."

"But what can be done?" came from all sides.

"I've heard it said in Old England," said Dame Cook, "that a ghost that roams restlessly can be quieted by burial in the earth, even as the body was, and so insure its rest even as that of the body."

The good preacher of the town agreed with Mistress Cook, and so did all the others. Nay, they were ready to agree to anything that would take away the angry ghost from their midst.

So the preacher set the burial day for the ghost, to take the trouble from among them.

The gravediggers were ordered to dig a grave under the old poplar tree where the ghost had been seen by Peter and David.

On the set day, which was a Friday, all the people of

the town gathered around the church. The preacher came from the holy house, with the pallbearers walking slowly before him. Then they formed into a solemn procession, moving through the roads and green that led to the ancient poplar, where they stopped around the open grave.

The church bell from the little church tolled, and the good minister spoke the burial service for the ghost of Chief Justice Chew, bidding him rest in peace until the great day of resurrection.

The earth was thrown onto the grave, and each one went home in hopeful silence.

That evening some hardy Dover men returned cautiously on the road past the big poplar that led to the Inn of King George III. Heaven be praised! There was no ghost to be seen anywhere.

Great was the rejoicing by all, and from that day on the ghost of Chief Justice Chew was never seen again, no matter how much kachewing or hard chewing any man, woman, or child ever did in Dover town.

Arnsy Maull,
the Conjure Man

GOIN' tell you 'bout Arnsy Maull, the wizard o' Bell-town in Delaware.

Folks said he sold his soul to the Devil to become a conjure man; some said he learned conjurin' from his grandfather come from Afriky on a stinkin' slave ship. Don't matter how he learned, it never stopped folks round Belltown far as Lewes by the ocean, black an' white, to ask help from Arnsy, the conjure man.

Now, goin' tell you how he helped a fine, young fellow git a girl who wouldn't marry him nohow, though he promised her a golden chariot with white horses t' ride.

That young fellow's name was Charlie, and his best friend was Tom. There wasn't a thing Charlie didn't tell Tom, so he told him 'bout Laura, a pretty young girl of Lewes he loved, but who'd have none o' him.

Poor Charlie, he was that much in love he believed if he didn't marry Laura the world would come t' an end. But she favored a city man.

One day them two, Charlie and Tom, were talkin' 'bout this. Said Tom:

"Charlie, why don't you go t' see Arnsy Maull. Folks say he kin help any man that's in trouble an' cure any sickness an' make ghosts rush over the marshes. He's got snake oil an' blood o' black cats t' help stop fits. He's a true conjurin' man an' kin straighten any trouble."

"I don't like t' go t' wizards," Charlie said.

"Ain't scared, are you? Maybe ye're scared o' Laura, too."

"No, I ain't scared at all. Just don't fancy havin' anythin' to do with wizards," says Charlie.

"Well, then you just come on an' bring five dollars an' a little brown jug that's full. If you bring that to Arnsy Maull, the Wizard o' Belltown, you sure goin' git Laura."

Tom, he talked a little more, an' in the end Charlie said he'd go. "Let's go tonight when I'm through with my work," he said.

These two, Charlie an' Tom, met that night on Knittin' Street an' walked through Frog Alley while that wind was rushin' like a haunt right into the marshes.

They walked an' walked along the road, an' when they came past the cemetery the wind was chasin' black clouds in the sky t' beat Jerusalem.

They come t' Belltown, where there was shacks and fine, white houses with space in between for growin' weeds an' greens.

They walked along the path, swayin' an' swingin' with the wind while lightnin' bugs was dancin' on the marsh. So they came where Arnsy Maull, the Wizard o' Belltown, lived all alone.

There was a light peepin' through the chinks.

Tom knocked on the door and never waited t' hear "come in." He pushed the door open an' walked right in with Charlie.

There was Arnsy Maull sittin' by the little stove full o' bright kindlin', an' on the little table was a candle.

Arnsy Maull's place was a queer ol' place. There were boxes an' shelves all around with bottles an' roots an' herbs that'd help people in their miseries. There were splinters come from a tree struck by lightnin' 'd stop any toothache, an' there were pebbles that'd keep away sickness from ol' men. There were so many things I couldn't begin to tell you.

Said Arnsy Maull, sittin' by the fire, though it was a warm June day:

"Good ee'n gen'men. You come for somethin'?"

" 'Deed we do," said Tom. "Charlie here needs your help."

"There's many 's come for help right here. All kinds o' folks. Black folks an' white folks. Now, what's yoh trouble, young man?"

Didn't take long an' Charlie told his troubles 'bout his wantin' to marry Laura and she'd have none o' him because he was only a Delaware oysterman while she was aimin' for a city feller.

Arnsy Maull listened, never said a word, just twitchin' his little black eyes an' said nothin'.

When Charlie was done, Arnsy just sat studyin' the

stove but never said a word, like his mouth was full o' teeth.

All you heard was the cracklin' o' the wood in the stove that hot summer night. 'Twas warm enough to give you a bath without a river.

Tom an' Charlie were wonderin' how come Arnsy never opened his mouth, just blinked his black eyes an' just hummed to hisself:

> Ol' Abe Lincoln wuz a good ol' man,
> Er good old man wuz e-e,
> 'E broke de bonds ob er slavery
> Un e-e set the black man free.

By the time Arnsy reached the end o' that song Tom knew exactly what was the trouble. He poked Charlie in the ribs an' said, whisperin'-like:

"Y' fergot to give Arnsy what you brung along to help 'm. Charlie, give Arnsy what you brung."

Then Charlie took the little brown jug he had an' a bran' new five-dollar bill an' give it quick to Arnsy.

Arnsy took it an' never said a word 'bout it.

Then he studied the fire some more an' turned his black eyes on Charlie and said:

"I knows all 'bout yuh trouble an' kin help yuh easy."

He got up from his stool and walked to a shelf that was on the wall, opened a wooden box, an' took somethin' from it. He brung it to Charlie an' held it high up 'gainst the candlelight.

An' what d' you think it was—only three thin hairs!

Then he took a piece o' newspaper an' put the hairs in. He give it to Charlie. Then he said:

"You take this here hair an' bury it in the ground right near where that gal Laura lives an' say three times, 'Git away from dar! Git away from dar! Git away from dar!' That'll send away them thoughts Laura's got 'bout marryin' the city feller, an' she'll marry you quick instead."

Charlie an' Tom went away, an' Charlie did exactly as Arnsy, the conjure doctor of Belltown told him. On a dark night he buried the hair in a lot back o' Laura's house an' said three times, "Git away from dar! Git away from dar! Git away from dar!"

Sure 'nough, jest one month later, when Charlie came and asked Laura with the blue eyes t' go to church with 'm for marryin', she was sweet 's honey. So they went to church, got married, an' lived happy ever after.

Not long after that Arnsy Maull stopped bein' a conjure man.

Come one night there was a great storm, an' Arnsy tol' all his friends that he wouldn't be no conjurin' man no more an' wouldn't have anythin' t' do with the Devil no more if his friends 'd go out at night with long black snake whips whippin' the Devil away and lettin' the Lord come in.

His friends, they did just that, and from that time on Arnsy Maull was no more a wizard but a good churchgoin', prayin' man.

When Arnsy Maull died, the wind screamed through

Lewes and Belltown as it never did from the time of Adam, pullin' fifty-year-old trees from the ground. That was the Devil screamin' 'cause he couldn't fetch Arnsy Maull's soul. He went to a better place.

Amen.

PENNSYLVANIA
The Keystone State

Joe Magerack, the Steel-Mill Man

PENNSYLVANIA is a great big state, with great big rivers and great big mountains, great big coal fields and great big forests—and great big Joe Magerack.

They tell about him along the valleys of the Allegheny River and along the hills of the Monongahela, where the blue iron grows in the black earth. They tell about Joe Magerack, who was so big he was born in two countries, in old Hungary and in the new, young, green U.S.A.

He was a true American. He wanted to live in the shiny land of freedom where there was more of plenty than anywhere in the world. He was big as Paul Bunyan and just as strong, and folks love to tell the things he did when they gather for feasting and dancing.

Now, open your ears, open your eyes, and listen with both of 'em.

One fine day Joe Magerack came to the mountains of Pennsylvania, to the Furnace towns, the Bloomer Steel Mills, where they melted steel and poured it into dollies and sent them over the land to build up great America.

He came to the mill foreman for a job. The foreman took one look and saw a man who could do as much as ten steelworkers from old Hungary, from the old Slav land, put together, and he took him on right then and there.

The hunkie huskies in the mills looked at Joe and asked him how he got there. They asked him from where he came, what he wanted to do, who his father was, who his mother was, and who his relatives were. They asked him where he was born and what was his name.

"My name is Joe Magerack," he roared, "I want work, eat, an' drink. Don't want no sleep, never."

He tore open his shirt and showed his iron chest and iron arms. The hunkies looked, and their eyes opened big as saucers.

"No man like that came from the *putztas* of the old, old Magyar land."

Joe laughed and bellowed like an ox, "A leetle piece of me from dat old country, a beeg chunk of me from here in iron country. I come in ore car right here an' I sleep in ore pile near furnace an' I look like ore, so it's all right. Now I want work in ore."

To work he went, and the mill foreman and the hunkies saw work they never saw before.

Joe worked like fifty men and never 'd rest or sleep. He never played like the other men. He roared, "Work, that is play," and made two thousand pounds of steel a day, pushed two thousand pounds of steel with his little

finger, and lifted dolly bars of steel two thousand pounds
in weight.

That was a man, Joe Magerack.

When he was through working he'd go home to Mrs.
Horkey, who fed him.

She made mountains of "paprikash" made of meat and
potatoes and onions and tubs full of red, powdered paprikash. But what he loved most was meat and rice with
nice green cabbage leaves all around!

One day there was a great party because Mary, Steve
Mestrovic's pretty daughter, got married. After the party
everybody had a headache from dancing and drinking
prunejack.

Joe's head ached, too, but he went to work just the
same, and when he became hungry he sent the mill boy to
Mrs. Horkey to say he was coming for dinner, for plenty
of meat and rice stuffed in cabbage leaves.

Mrs. Horkey, she liked Joe and loved to feed him.

She boiled a couple of bushels of cabbages and got
ready mountains of ground red meat and spices. Then she
went to cook the rice.

Mrs. Horkey was still a little dizzy from Steve's party
so she put the whole barrelful of rice into the big iron
kettles instead of just a couple of pails full.

Then she sat down in the rocking chair to wait for the
rice to cook. She rocked back and forth, back and forth,
and soon she fell asleep while the rice began to cook and
boil. Her head dropped on her bosom, and she snored
like a sawmill while the rice kept on cooking and swelling.

Mrs. Horkey had a beautiful dream of angels and the Holy Lord as the swelling rice fell out of the pots and covered the floor.

It covered her legs, but she kept on sleeping. It came up to her knees, it came up to her chest, but she snored peacefully. It covered her face and eyes, it came out of the window, and her nearest neighbor Mrs. Hlavanka saw it. She rushed to the window, took one look, and ran to the mill, shouting on the top of her voice:

"Mrs. Horkey is drownin' in the rice she is cookin' for Joe! Mrs. Horkey is drownin' in the rice she is cookin' for Joe!"

The hunkies and Joe ran from the mill. They ran to the house, where the rice was pouring out of the windows and doors like a blanket of snow.

"Tear down the house or we'll never save Mrs. Horkey," cried some.

Bellowed Joe, "Foolish talk, I know better way," and he began to eat the rice at the door while men and women stood around watching.

Joe ate through the door, ate through the sides, and he ate all around. Soon you could see the picture of the Holy Mother on the wall. Next you could see the face of Mrs. Horkey; then her bosom, and soon . . . she leaped up, took Joe by the hand, and made him dance a chardash, so happy was she to be alive and dancing. Then all the company danced and drank prunejack just as if it were another wedding, forgetting all about the iron melting in the furnaces.

Suddenly the mill foreman ran up all out of breath, shouting, "Lazy louts, come quick, there's trouble in furnace No. 7!" That was Joe's furnace.

Hunkies dropped their partners, Joe his plate, and all raced to the mill.

The white-hot metal in No. 7 was roaring and hissing with heat hotter than hottest, and the bricks were groaning and crackling. A small seam showed, and the furnace was ready to bust wide open. It would ruin the furnace and would ruin the metal in it, and maybe burn people, too. Men began to run.

"Don't run," Joe roared: "I fix it. Watch me!"

He ran to the red-hot bricks, put his giant iron arms around 'em and his iron chest against 'em, and pulled and strained with all his might, then held it tight together. He got red in the face, and steam came from his nose, but he held on tight, until the seam closed and welded from its own heat so no metal could pour out.

The hunkies cheered, and the mill foreman roared, "Now you can go back to your eating and dancing."

The mill hands, they didn't need coaxing, and soon they were again at Mrs. Horkey's, having the time of their lives dancing and drinking in honor of Joe Magerack, the hero of the day.

And a hero he has remained ever since in the steel mills of Pennsylvania in the valleys of the Allegheny and the hills of the Monongahela.

True Love in the Blue Mountains

IN THE beautiful Blue Mountains, in the wild Blue Mountains of Pennsylvania along the rushing Schuylkill River, there lived young farmer Johan. He was big, strong, and handsome, and no man could work nor hunt better than he.

Johan loved Hilda of Tulpehocken in the Wild Blue Mountains, and their wedding day was set.

The groom set out early in the morning on his best horse, Strongheart, dressed in his finest, with silver buckles and gilded buttons, to be with his bride a day before the wedding—but it was to be otherwise.

Soon the sky grew black, the wind blew fierce, the rain came thick as sheets, and Johan had to stop at an inn.

The storm passed, and the sky was empty of clouds and water. Thunder and lightning ceased, the wind died down, and a strange, torn, thick mist came up winding around trees and rocks, grass and ferns. It looked like the lost spirits of white men and Indians winding their way through dripping trunks and looming rocks.

"Don't go tonight," the host of the tavern said. "Wild spirits are running loose in the mountains. You might meet the King of the Wolves. He has seven horns on his wolf's head, and he is one-third bear and one-third panther."

"I'm not afraid of any beast. I must go to Hilda, my bride."

"Don't go tonight," said the host, "there are evil spirits abroad."

But Johan mounted Strongheart and went out on the dark road.

The hoot-owl hooted mournfully in the gray-white mist, and catamounts shrilled, their wild cries tearing the fog to shreds. Wolves howled and frogs croaked, but Johan went on his way—he was not afraid.

They came near the rushing, roaring Schuylkill.

"On, Strongheart, on!" the bridegroom whispered to his horse. "Soon you'll be in a warm stall with sweet-smelling hay before you, and Hilda will give it to you."

The horse understood and kept on till they reached a giant chestnut near the place easiest to ford.

The horse stopped, for even there the river was swollen and running wildly enough to frighten beast and man.

"On, Strongheart, we are not afraid. We must reach Hilda tonight. My guardian spirit watches over us; no harm can befall us."

The horse plunged into the roaring river, nostrils wide open, head high and neck strained. Above them wild mists rolled and floated.

They reached the middle of the stream, and a giant log moved their way. It would crush them with its weight! The horse let out a whinnying scream, and Johan cried out, "Help, my good spirit! Help or I am lost! Hilda is waiting for me!"

The log came nearer . . . swirling wildly . . . nearly touched them . . . when a torn mist like a great strong hand lifted them both high over the soaring Schuylkill, over the giant log and . . . they were at the entrance of a large cavern all lit and marvelous to behold. The mist that carried Johan and his horse became a tall and living being, dressed in a long gray cloak . . . but the face seemed in a distant cloud.

"Come," said the misty figure in a far voice, "I am your guardian spirit. I came to help you when you called me, and now I'll lead you to our King."

They went along a wondrous street lined with palaces of precious stones, with lovely gardens where gilded birds sang songs to melt the heart, till they came to a large green, where stood a golden throne. On it sat the King, in dazzling clothes, a jeweled crown on his head, and around him stood the courtiers all dressed in gleaming clothes. But their faces could not be seen clearly. They all seemed far away and cloudy. . . . Johan thought they looked like knights in books his parents had brought from the old country, only different.

"Where am I?" he asked.

"In the land where men never grow old. Stay with us."

"I can't stay," said Johan. "My bride is waiting in Tulpehocken. We are to be married tomorrow."

"Then stay with us just for the night. There is a grand celebration."

What could Johan say?

He stayed to feast and danced all night, and though he was close to those with whom he feasted, he never saw clearly a single face.

Dawn came.

"Now I must go to my bride, great King!"

"Don't return," the King urged. "You'll be sorry if you do."

"I must go to my bride," Johan cried.

"Go you may, but you must return!"

Strong, shrouded hands lifted him high, and in an instant he was again on the banks of the Schuylkill River in the Blue Mountains of Pennsylvania.

The sun shone warm, the birds sang sweet, trees and grass and flowers were all around, but everything seemed so different!

He rode swiftly to Tulpehocken, full of love, full of happy excitement for his wedding.

Soon he came to the open green before his bride's home. There sat a lovely old lady on a rocking chair with gay children all around her.

Strongheart stopped, and Johan looked at the old lady. She looked so familiar.

The lady rose and came to him while the children

looked on, openmouthed. When she got to the horse every drop of blood went from her face.

"Johan," she cried.

"That's my name. Where is Hilda my bride? This is our marriage day."

The old lady stood still for a moment, then she said, "Wait, first I must send the children away."

There was a tone in her voice that made him obey.

She turned to the children and in a whispering voice told them to go home and not to say a word about the man on the horse dressed in strange, old-fashioned clothes with silver buckles and large gilt buttons.

The children left, and she returned to Johan.

"You want Hilda?" she asked.

"Yes," he said eagerly.

"I am Hilda; I am Hilda, and you are Johan!"

There was no color in his face, only terror in his eyes.

"I am Hilda, and I have been waiting for you for more than sixty years. I knew some evil spirit kept you from me."

"I was away only a single night . . . in a cave . . . where there is a King with a jeweled crown," Johan said in a whisper.

"No, not a single night, but more than sixty years! It seemed to you only a single night. The spirits of the Mountains held you."

"Then let us go at once to a priest to marry us, Hilda." He knew it was she.

"I can't marry you now, Johan. I am too old. We can only be married in heaven."

"No, we will marry now."

"That you can't do," and next to him stood the shrouded figure that brought him to the cave. "You have been to our land of eternal youth, where years are only minutes, and now you must return."

Then Hilda spoke slowly and sadly, "I waited for Johan all these years, and you had him all the time. You might leave him on this earth, where I have but little time more."

Said the voice softly, "You'll have him all the years to the end of time, and you'll be joined in the greater world."

Then he lifted Johan and his horse and . . . they were gone!

Hilda stayed but a little on this earth, so anxious was she to join her bridegroom.

She died. That's what people said. But she did not die at all. She just left this world to join Johan in the greater world.

Along the Monongahela

THERE is a river in Pennsylvania with the most beautiful name in the American language—maybe in any language—and that name is Monongahela. Folks call the land around that river God's own country, and a truer word was never said.

Up and down the shining waters of the Monongahela there have sailed bateaux, flatboats, keel boats, and steamboats; and river men, passengers, and roustabouts have worked and fought and sung and wept there.

One glorious morning the *Chieftain* and the *Bennet*, as fine two boats as ever floated, were ready to start from Pittsburgh wharf.

Now, there was always no end of rivalry between captains and crews, and the captains of these boats were out to see which vessel was faster than the other.

There were shouts and cries at the wharf, and each crew tried to work faster and get more passengers than the other.

A woman with a babe in her arms and baggage by her side stood waiting to go on board. Up rushed a man from the *Bennet* and got hold of the babe, up rushed a man from the *Chieftain* and grabbed the woman and her baggage, and before the woman could open her mouth she was on one boat with baggage, and her child was on the other. The boats started with screaming of whistles and yelling and shouting of crews and riders. But loudest of all were the screams of the woman on one boat and the wailing of the babe in the arms of the river man on the other.

Her screaming and weeping were of little use, for the captains were bent on racing to see who would reach Elizabeth town first.

"Captain! Captain! I want my child," the distracted woman cried.

"You'll get your child when we beat that tub to Elizabeth town," the captain roared.

The child in the arms of the river man screamed and yowled, and the crew made fun of the fellow who carried it.

"Stop the boat so I can get rid of the squalling brat," he bellowed.

"Y' kin roar, an' the brat kin squall, but the *Bennet* goes on an'll beat that dancin' tub limpin' down the river."

The *Chieftain* and the *Bennet* raced side by side with the passengers in full excitement about it.

A man who planned to get off halfway didn't, to see that race to the end. A man who had a mule to be delivered had his mule thrown overboard to swim to land as best it could. But the boats raced as the smokestacks belched smoke and the Monongahela churned a song which the river men understood and the boatmen sang:

> Some rows up, but we rows down,
> All the way from Pittsburgh town.
> Pull away, pull away. . . .

The whistles screamed to drive off the Devil and bring good luck as the boats raced on.

White folks, black folks stood along the shore, cheering themselves hoarse. Even the mother crying for her child forgot her anger for a time.

The boats raced fiercely, the fire sparks flew from the stacks.

They were neck and neck, and there was a din as if the end of the world had come when those boats neared the locks.

The *Bennet* was ahead, the *Chieftain* close behind, and there was the end of the race.

The good boat *Bennet* won by a good boat length.

Passengers cheered, river men huzzahed, and all were mighty glad, even the woman, now with the child in her arms.

That was a day on the Monongahela, the river with the most beautiful name in all the American language!

The Hex and the Oxen

IN THE days gone by, when hex women and witch doctors had things their way in Pennsylvania, particularly around the Blue Mountains, there lived a farmer and his wife in those parts who loved gold more than they loved God. Sure that farmer woman was a witch, there was no question about it, and there wasn't a thing she wouldn't do, white or black, to add to her pile of gold. She'd shortweigh butter and cheese, and she would lie about the age of her chickens; she'd fill the bottom of her apple bushels with straw and lie about the hay—she wouldn't stop at anything to feel the clinking of money in her hands. She and her husband.

Folks soon found out which way the wind blew, and none would buy or barter with them. None would even speak to them. So they lived by themselves, and no gold was coming in.

One early morning they sat outside on the porch talking. Said Katie, the woman, "I miss the clinking of money in my hands."

"I miss it, too," said her husband Ludwig. "But no one will buy anything from us or even speak to us."

"But we fooled them for a long time, didn't we?" said she, and both had a good laugh.

"And I'll fool them more," she added. "I have studied the hexing books I found in the old barn, and I have the Devil's power. Soon the yellow gold and white silver will roll again into our hands."

"You always had a smart head on you, Katie."

"Well, good husband, I'll show you the kind of head I really have. Before night we'll have plenty of money again."

She mumbled magic words and made circles. . . . A wind blew up—and Ludwig, the farmer with the red beard, was a fine, fat, sleek, brown ox! Sleek as if he had been fed the finest grain and hay.

Katie ran to neighbors and told everybody she had a fine, strong ox for sale. Before the sun stood in the middle of the sky farmers and butchers came to look at the beast.

"That ox has lived on the fat of the land," the butcher man said.

"So he has," Katie replied.

"Where is Ludwig?" another one asked.

"Gone to Lebanon to look for more good cattle."

A man bought the animal and started home, feeling he had struck a good bargain.

Ox and man walked on the sunny-spotted road high up in the Blue Mountains. They reached the top, and there was a sight fit for paradise. The man stopped to see the broad valleys and the tidy farms, when a wind blew up. He turned around . . . the ox was gone. . . .

He ran up and he ran down and he ran all around, but all his running did him little good—that ox was gone. And a man was walking down the road.

He got others to help him search, but no ox could be found. In the end he went home cursing the hour he bought the beast.

In the evening Katie and Ludwig were sitting by the candlelight counting the good money paid for the ox.

"It was so easy to fool that fellow," Katie said.

"You are a very smart woman, and I don't mind being an ox for a little while," Ludwig said.

Time went by, and then these two thought they'd like to feel some nice hard money in their horny hands again.

"Ludwig, my pet, we'll play the same little trick. I'll use my hex and fool the fools again."

She mumbled magic words and made circles. . . . A wind blew up—and there was the sleekest, fattest white ox you ever did see. As fine an ox as ever there was in all the Blue Mountains of Pennsylvania.

Katie ran around, far and wide, and soon all knew she had a fine, white ox for sale.

Men came and looked, and they said they never saw a finer animal. Katie asked little, and a sale was quickly made, and the man went off with his ox.

He went up the mountain. . . . A wind blew up . . . and the ox was gone! . . .

He searched high, he searched low, and he searched all around, but it did him little good. There was no ox to be seen. But a man was walking down the road.

He told his friends the tale, and folks shook their heads and said it was ill luck to buy anything from the hex woman on the mountain.

Weeks went by, sun and moon rolled around, and one morning Katie and Ludwig missed again the clinking of money in their horny hands.

"We'll make more soon," she cried. She made a circle, mumbled words . . . a wind blew up, and there stood a fine, fat, black ox. Then she ran everywhere and told folks she had the finest black ox for sale that was ever seen. Butchers and farmers came to see, but with wary eyes.

It truly was the finest, fattest, black ox ever seen, and a butcher man from Lebanon bought it. He tied a rope around the animal's head and started homeward together with a friend.

They were out aways when the Lebanon butcher man said to his friend:

"I'll drive the ox ahead, you follow a little ways behind. Don't take your eyes off that animal whatever happens. That ox'll not disappear this time."

When they got to the hill a wild wind blew up and the ox ran off—and the butcher's friend saw coming from the thicket red-bearded Ludwig. . . .

"From where did you come?" the butcher man asked.

Ludwig hemmed and hawed and mumbled and didn't know what to say.

Then the Lebanon man knew the truth.

"Your wife is a hex," he cried. "She hexed you to

become an ox and then changed you to cheat me. I'll have her before the judge and see her burn as a witch."

Ludwig ran off, and the butcher man went to court, accusing Katie of changing her husband into an ox to sell him and then change him back. She had cheated folks of their hard-earned money.

The judge made Katie and Ludwig pay back the money they had taken, but since no one could prove the woman a witch he let her go free. But he warned her if ever she was found hexing in the Blue Mountains it would go ill with her. Katie listened to the warning and did not hex her husband into an ox again.

Land of Wonders

BUCKS COUNTY in Pennsylvania is a county of great wonders. The land is rich as Paradise, and the doings are strange as morning dreams.

There, hoopsnakes roll on the ground till they make holes in the trees, pale-green animals swim, fly, run, and leap, and there are white rabbits as big as calves that can only be shot by a silver bullet.

On windy days in Bucks County, when the wind blows fiercely on the Hexenkopf, the Witch's Head mountain, fish from dark, still ponds leap wildly in the air. They fly high to heaven, come down the meadows, munch mountain mint and whortleberries, and then leap back into the water.

In that marvelous Bucks County there is a place called Dark Hollow, where there are no fish in the water though there are plenty of animals on the land. There, wild hooting owls turn into hornets, and strange beasts swallow their own heads, and weird giant specters, fifteen feet high, with shrouded faces, walk in the windy night.

In that county of wonders, in haunted Dark Hollow in Pennsylvania, there was young Hans, who worked faithfully for a farmer for his passage from the old country.

One noonday when the sun shone hot the master said to Hans:

"Hans, take the grain, go to the mill on the Neshaminy River, and have it ground fine white. Return before sunset, for I need you in the barn."

"That I will, master," said Hans.

He got on a fine, big horse, tied the sacks well behind the saddle, and rode fast to the gristmill on the river.

"Miller, grind that corn," he said, "a storm is on the way."

The miller ground the grain between big round stones, white and fine. Hans put it in the sacks, tied them behind his saddle, and got on his horse.

He rode along the giant hickory trees, along the tall red cedars. But the sky was darkening quickly.

He rode along the big mulberry trees, along the tall elms, when of a sudden a fierce wind began howling through the branches. It tore off his tall hat and blew it from tree to tree. It kept on flying high till it reached the Hexenkopf Mountain and disturbed some witches at their game. One grew angry and flew right into Hans's horse's mouth. The animal began to act as if the Devil had gotten into its inners.

It reared on its hind legs and began racing on the road. It tore laurel and juneberries, mountain mint and dittany—all that came in the way of its hoofs. Hans's face was ripped and whipped by branches, too.

A hole tore in one of the sacks, and the flour came out and covered horse and man all white. Hans's clothes and face and hair, the horse's mane and body and tail, all were a ghostly white.

Hans, yelling, his long white hair flying wildly in the screaming wind, and the galloping horse, a strange white all over, looked like witches coming from the Hexenkopf.

Flying Hans and flying horse had gone halfway up the hill when they met a wagon drawn by two strong horses in which sat three pretty young maidens going to an apple-cutting.

No sooner did they see that wild horseman with the flying hair, screaming and roaring, and his steed than a great fright fell upon them.

They knew they lived in a country where strange things happened, and here was sure proof of it. They turned near white at the sight of the white, yelling horseman and his white horse, whipped up their own animals, and reached the farm where they were bound for. There they told one and all they had seen a ghostly horseman and his ghostly steed coming from the Hexenkopf.

Everyone believed them, for didn't they live in Bucks County, where things happen stranger than dreams in the early morning?

Young John

IN THE years that have passed there lived at Harris Ferry, on the broad, rolling Susquehanna River, Old John and his three sons. The two eldest sons were big and strong and lazy, but the youngest, Young John, whom he loved best, was small and not too strong; yet he helped his father at work more than the others did.

One day when Old John felt his end was near, he called his sons to him and said, "Sons, my life is coming near the end, and soon I'll not be here. But before I go I want to give you each what I think is best for you.

"To you, my eldest son, I give my fine horse and saddle. Both have served me well, and I hope will serve you equally.

"To you, my next, I give my gun and lead and powder. They'll give you food and clothes even as they gave me.

"And to you, Young John, I give my little shack and fishing rod. They will give you food and shelter here at home, for you are not strong enough to travel or to battle."

Shortly after, Old John was in a better world.

For a time the three brothers lived together, hunting and fishing whenever they had mind to. One day the eldest brother said:

"I'm tired of riding along the shores of the Susquehanna. With my fine horse I can travel through the land and seek my fortune and adventure."

He saddled his horse and went out West, where Americans found fame and fortune. He became a soldier, for it was the quickest way to find adventure.

A little later the second brother said, "I, too, am tired of this quiet life on the Susquehanna. I want to be a rich man."

He took his gun and joined a band who held up people and broke the peace until they were captured and put where they could do no harm.

Young John worked hard and became friends with the Indians. He had what he needed and was contented to stay where he was.

One day he was sitting under a drooping willow tree, fishing in the rolling Susquehanna. Suddenly he felt a hard pull on his line, and soon he pulled out a giant shad with blue and silver gleaming scales. Young John threw him on the green grass, and the poor fish flung about and turned and twisted himself in pain and agony, looking with glassy eyes at his captor.

Young John, without even thinking, picked up the fish, flung him back into the water, and went home.

The next day Young John went fishing again. He caught pike and pickerel, sunfish and catfish. He had

about enough when he heard a great splashing, and there
was the big shad to whom he had given freedom. The shad
leaped and plunged about and then flung something from
his mouth right at Young John's feet. Young John saw
it was a bluish-black, gleaming, hard stone, the like of
which he had never seen before. He picked it up, and the
fish swam around as if waiting for something, but Young
John went home.

The next day Young John went fishing, as he did every
day. He caught a mess of fish, and there was the blue-and-
silver gleaming shad again. Again he flung a blue-black
stone at Young John's feet and kept swimming upstream,
as if to lead him somewhere.

This the shad kept doing day after day, and Young
John put away all the blue-black stones in a corner of
his shack.

One day he saw smoke over the trees of his home. He
ran quick as his legs would carry him and found it—
burned. Not a stick was left. All was black, except a
gleaming glow among the blue-black stones the shad had
given to Young John. The fire in these stones kept on
burning and burning for a long time, and Young John
could not understand it.

The next day he went fishing, for though he had no
roof over his head, he had to eat. There was the shad
again with one of the stones in his mouth, swimming back
and forth, as if going somewhere.

John saw this and understood. The fish would show

him where the black stones could be found. He packed his fishing rod and followed the fish.

For two full days the shad swam upstream and John followed. Then the fish left the broad Susquehanna and turned into a little river that went up the mountains and then . . . the shad disappeared. John looked up and down the river, but the shad was nowhere in sight. Soon some Indians came up, and he told them why he was there.

They led him to their village, where he saw the blue-black stones burning! When the fire was low the Indians added more of these stones.

They told him there were enough of them in the mountains to heat the Indian fires as long as the sun would shine!

Then John at last understood why the shad had led him up the river. The blue-black stones were a reward for sparing his life.

He built a raft and loaded it with the stones and steered it down the rolling Susquehanna as far as Harris Ferry, now called Harrisburg, the capital of Pennsylvania.

There he told all about the hard stones and how they burned better and longer than logs. He sold them to the settlers and went back for more. He kept on getting the black, hard stones—coal they were called—selling them, and so became a rich man. And all because of an act of kindness, for kindness is a seed from which riches grow.

A Trickster Tricks
the Devil

ON THE roads roamed Eileschpijjel, and a merrier fellow there never was in all the Quaker State. He brought laughter to folks wherever he went and played tricks in every place. He feared neither man nor beast nor hex nor Devil. Up and down and all around the state he wandered and was welcome wherever he went.

One day Eileschpijjel walked along the path, stick in hand, when he saw the Devil coming his way ready for mischief and trouble.

The Devil and Eileschpijjel had fought many a battle, and the Devil was always beaten, but he was ever ready to try again.

The two walked along the roads, between the mountains, through the woods, talking till they came to a farmhouse, where there wasn't a soul to be seen. Farmer and family had gone to the fair.

Eileschpijjel and the Devil sat down near the spring to have their noonday meal.

"Eileschpijjel, you're pretty smart, and you have

beaten me many a time, but there is one thing in which you can't beat me."

"Maybe I can and maybe I can't; I trust my wits and my good luck. Now, tell me in what can't I beat you."

"You can never stand the heat I can stand, for my home is hotter than a white-heated, steel-mill furnace."

"Maybe I can and maybe I can't, but I am willing to try it once," said the trickster of Pennsylvania.

"Let's try it right now," the Devil cried. "There's a stove here by the house. We'll put logs in it and get it going, then we'll both get in and see who can stay longest. If you can't stay there as long as I, you belong to me."

Eileschpijjel agreed. They gathered chestnut logs and oak logs, pine logs and maple logs, and put them all in the stove. Then they started the fire. The Devil crept in, Eileschpijjel following, closing the door behind them.

The fire began to burn, and the stove was getting hot. The fire burned higher, and the stove was getting hotter. The fire burned and roared, and bricks were getting burning hot.

The Devil sat back happy and contented, but Eileschpijjel was mighty uncomfortable. He was sweating all over and moved from place to place.

The oven was becoming hotter and hotter, the bricks were red, and Eileschpijjel's pants began to burn. He couldn't stand the heat any more. He began crawling to the door to get out.

"Where are you going?" the Devil cried. "Can't stand

the heat? Remember, if you run, you can't run far, for you belong to me."

"Can't stand the heat! Don't talk so foolish! Fact is, I am freezing cold and shivering in my skin. I am going out to put on bigger logs. I want to get warmed up." And Eileschpijjel slid out of the door.

The Devil scratched his head and thought hard. Soon he, too, slid out of the stove.

There was Eileschpijjel, busy gathering big spruce logs to put in the stove.

Said the Devil angrily, "Don't get the logs. I am beginning to think you're a fellow that can't be beat. But let me think, and some day I'll try again."

The Devil went off grumbling, and Eileschpijjel went off singing, playing pranks, and making merry to bring pleasure to the people in the lovely state of Pennsylvania.

The Wolf-Bride

STRANGE stories run like cobwebs through our land, and none more strange than those heard in the South Mountains of Pennsylvania—and none can tell them better than Henry of a Thousand Tales.

Tells Henry:

In those mountains lived young Harman, whose greatest pleasure was hunting and fishing. One day he took his gun and went hunting up Wolf Camp Run, where the trees stood close and the shadows were weird.

The sun could not come through the leaves, and the wind was low and whining, but Harman walked on until he reached the deserted, haunted mill where everyone feared to go.

Suddenly a large wolf with gleaming eyes and long hair stood on the road.

Harman stopped in his tracks, as if turned to stone, nor did he raise his gun, for the hexing Harsh fever struck him like a thunderbolt, the fever that paralyzes hands and feet. There was a silver bullet in his vest for shooting witches, but he could not get it. He looked at the big, black wolf and the wolf looked at him.

Then the big, shaggy beast turned slowly and trotted toward the haunted mill, now and then looking backward. It went right up to the black entrance of the mill, looked once again at Harman, and disappeared.

Life came back to Harman's limbs. He quickly loaded his gun with the silver bullet and walked toward the mill. That wolf was no common wolf, Harman knew, it was a hexed beast, and no common bullet could hurt it.

Holding his gun straight before him, he came to the opening of the mill. A pair of fiercely gleaming eyes looked out of the dark. He raised his gun to his shoulder and . . . again turned still as stone! The Harsh fever flowed in his limbs and he could not move hand or foot!

At the door stood the loveliest girl he ever saw. Her eyes were black diamonds and her black hair reached to the ground. Harman knew she was a witch, a hexed creature!

Spoke the girl, "Please help me. I am in great trouble. I came here with friends. They went berrying while I went swimming in the mill pond. When I came out my clothes were gone. Dishonest folks took them. I don't know what to do."

Life and speech came back to Harman. He knew she was lying, but it did not matter. He had fallen in love with her great beauty, and, no matter what she said, he loved her just the same.

"Take my coat," he cried eagerly. "Come with me to the house of my sisters. They will take good care of you."

She took the coat, and they walked along the paths, chatting gaily.

He forgot she was a witch. He thought only of her black eyes and red lips, her long hair and white throat. Nothing else mattered.

Harman's sisters welcomed the girl with open arms. They fed her, petted her, and put her to sleep in the loft in a soft feather bed.

Below, Harman sat still knowing full well his love was a witch! Maybe a werewolf! But he loved her and wanted her just the same. She must never leave, never turn into wolf again!

There was only one way to keep her from it. He knew the way. He heard it from a hexmaster!

He went to the barn, took hammer and nails, and ran out into the night. The moon shone sharp and gleaming. It was a hex moon, but the strongest hex of all was in Harman. He was in love with the girl, with her black eyes and long black hair and pale white face!

He never saw the moon, nor did he hear the lovely nightsong of the whippoorwills and the little creatures. He ran across the meadows, across the fields, till he reached the black woods, and soon he was up in Wild Wolf Camp and stood before the haunted mill. He ran all around it, and suddenly, when a shaft of silvery white light crept through the dark leaves, he saw on the floor a black pelt with long hair! The wolf's skin that had covered the girl with the black eyes and white face!

He leaped on it! It felt harsh in his hand and pricked

his fingers, but he put it against the old wheel and nailed
it down. Tight! Tight! The nails went through the skin!
Through the planks!

"Now she cannot leave me. Now she must stay!" he
said fiercely. "She cannot leave so long as I have her hex
clothes where she can't get them."

Then he went home, but he could not sleep thinking
of his beautiful love with the black eyes and white face
and of the mill up in Wolf Camp with the wolf's skin
nailed to the mill wheel.

The sun looked over the trees, and Harman was up and
awake. Soon the wolf girl came down the ladder, paler
than the cold white moon. Her black eyes were restless
and fierce.

"Didn't you sleep?" Harman cried.

"Not too well, but I'll be well soon enough."

She laughed a harsh little laugh that sounded like
broken bells.

"Will you stay here?"

"I came to stay only for a night, but now I must stay
here long." Her jet-black eyes went through Harman
like knives.

She stayed and worked and talked like all folks, but
she rarely smiled and was always cross. People were
scared of her. Even when Harman married her she was
no different, but he loved her just the same and would
do anything to please her or bring a smile to her white
face and black eyes.

One fine day he went fishing and wandered up to Wolf Camp to the haunted mill.

There on the wheel the wolf's skin was still nailed tight and taut. Harman looked at it and thought how there never was a smile on his wife's face for him.

"Perhaps if I take out the nails from the skin she will be kind and love me. It is shabby and worn, and she can't use it to turn wolf again."

He tore off the skin and threw it in the slow-moving dark water, and it floated slowly away. Then he sat down to fish.

Soon he heard a song, and there came along the path a strange company, a band of Indians. In their midst was a man with hands tied in the back. His hair was black and his eyes were black and there was a wild look in them. The same look was in his own wolf-bride's eyes. Maybe he was a She-kener, a gypsy from the hexed forest of Germany. He was roaring on top of his voice a Christmas song, though it was the time of the Indian summer.

> In the porch of Bethlehem
> Have crept the gypsies wild.
> They have stolen the swaddling clothes,
> Of the newborn child.
>
> Oh, those swarthy gypsies!
> How did the devils dare?
> They haven't left the holy child
> A stitch of clothes to wear.

This black-eyed fellow had murdered an Indian, and the tribe was taking him to the great father in Washington for permission to punish him as he deserved.

They went on their way, and Harman continued fishing.

The wolf-bride was hoeing the garden, and her eyes were like a black pool torn by a storm. Her body was bent and tired, and she hated all the world. She hated her human life, she wanted to roam the wild woods as a . . . wild wolf. . . .

Suddenly she felt a thrill in all her body. Her white skin under her drab dress felt fresh as after a bath. Into her eyes came a wild, moist gleam, as when she roamed the wild mountains. The deep nails in her wolfskin were gone!

She straightened up, unwound her long hair, and let the cool wind in it.

What made her feel as free as she used to feel in the woods? What was it?

Down the hill came the band of Indians, the prisoner in their midst. He was singing his wild song:

> Oh, those swarthy gypsies,
> How did the devils dare?
> They didn't leave the holy child
> A stitch of clothes to wear.

She didn't really hear the words, she just saw his deep, black eyes, and she saw his blue-black hair and the wild look in his face.

Maybe he was a She-kener, or maybe he was a wolf-man, but it did not matter to her; she felt he was a creature like herself who wanted to be wild and free. She ran up to him.

"He is my true love, and I go wherever he goes," she said to the Indians.

The prisoner laughed, showing white, gleaming wolf's teeth, and cried, "Then follow me right now."

So she went off with the black-eyed prisoner and the Indian band.

Harman came back with a mess of fish, but his wolf-bride was not there. Neighbors said she had gone off with the prisoner.

Then Harman told where he had found her and that she was a hexed wolf-woman not fit to live with respectable folks.

None believed him. Folks said it was slanderous talk to hide his shame and anger at his wife who left him, and folks were right and so was he.

Big Ghost, Little Ghost—
Who's Scared of a Ghost?

IN THE big city of Philadelphia, in the city of brotherly love, there are many, many people and many, many tales.

> One to begin,
> Two to show,
> Three to make ready,
> Four to go.

Once there lived a farmer right outside of that city, and he had a farmhand, Sam by name.

> Sam was little, Sam was strong,
> Sam 'd sing the whole day long.

But Sam worked only when he had a mind to, and then he worked mighty good. The rest of the time he liked best to lazy around and whittle wood, or maybe spin yarns or listen to stories.

All day long the farmer kept shouting, "Milk the cows! Haul the manure! Cut the hay! Cut the logs!" But he did little himself.

Sam 'd listen and never raise a hand till he was good and ready.

One afternoon farmer Bill roared, "Sam, fetch the cows, time for milkin'."

Sam lay in the meadow, looking at the sky turning gold and green.

"Hey, Sam, scared o' bringin' in the cows 'cause the big black bull's with 'em?"

"Ain't scared o' nothin'," Sam said. "I'll bring in the cattle in good time 's I always done. When the Devil's scoldin' he calls it work."

"Y're al'ays quotin' the Devil, Sam. Ain't y' afeared he'll fetch y' one day?"

"Fear's a slinkin', lazy cat. Ain't afeared o' the Devil, an' I ain't scared o' work with my hands instead o' makin' music with my chin."

Sam brought in the cows and milked them good, threw them forks full o' hay, cleaned the barn, fed the horses, and put the sheep in the pen.

The stars danced in the sky, the katydids and the whippoorwills and tree frogs sang their nightsong, and Sam was getting ready to go home.

And what do you think Farmer Bill was doing all this time? Helping Sam at his work? Not he.

He went into the house, got him a big white sheet, and covered himself from head to foot.

"Now I'll stand at God's acre where Sam goes passin' by, and we'll see if he ain't scared like he says he ain't."

But while Bill wound his sheet around him he didn't see

Jocko, the monkey he'd bought not long before from a circus man at the fair, stand in the corner and put around himself a big white tablecloth.

Monkey did what master did.

Farmer Bill went to the big gate of the cemetery and stood there waiting, waiting for Sam to pass.

Jocko went to the little gate of the cemetery and stood waiting, waiting like his master. Both stood waiting, looking like two white ghosts enough to scare a body white.

The moon was riding in the sky, and Sam came walking on the road, humming "The Hangsman's Tree."

> Slack your rope, hangsman,
> Oh, slack it for a while;
> I think I see my Father coming,
> Riding for many a mile.

So he came to God's Acre, and in the blue moonlight he saw the big ghost standing at one gate and the little ghost standing at the other.

He looked at the big ghost at one gate and looked at the little ghost at the other gate and just laughed.

Then he cried out loud:

"Big ghost's scared t' walk in the dark, so he took little ghost t' keep 'm company!" and he pointed at both.

Farmer Big-Ghost Bill looked to the gate where Sam was pointing and saw the little ghost—monkey Jocko covered with a white tablecloth. It scared him t' death.

"It's a ghost!" he bellowed, and began to run with wings on his feet.

Little Sam laughed and held his sides. Big-Ghost Bill ran, and Little-Ghost-Jocko was at his heels.

"Y' kin run faster 'n huntin' hound," cried Sam with laughing tears in his eyes, "but y' can't run away from fear. . . ."

Big-Ghost Bill ran, Little-Ghost-Jocko after him. They ran through meadows and they ran through fields and all around Philadelphia, and, if they haven't stopped running, you'll see them to this day running around the city of brotherly love.

The Good Witch-Doctor in the Mountains

UP IN the lovely Blue Mountains lived a good witch doctor. He was a little man, his face was full of wrinkles, and he had long, yellow teeth. No witch doctor was more famous than he, for he had studied the ancient books he dug out of the earth in the mountain one stormy night while blue flames and yellow snakes danced all around.

He and his little round wife lived in an old log house with twelve black cats, a black cow, black hens, a black rooster, and a black helping man.

Folks came to him to help them find water and find things that were lost; to avenge wrongs and to dig for treasures. He aided lovers in their plight, people who were sick, and he could cure animals and charm snakes. He could do all these things from reading these ancient secret books. For these reasons he was famous in every home and town in the Blue Mountains.

Preachers preached against him, and ministers said he was in league with evil forces. Folks listened to the sermons and then came to the little witch doctor just the same when they needed help.

One early morning one of his neighbors, a farmer, went to the barn and saw that the fine, new black oilcloth he had bought to cover his wagon and which he left hanging on the rafters was gone.

Many things were gone from barn and house of late and from the barns and houses of others nearby. They blamed the Pine Creek folks, the lazy people who lived in the swamps all around and who worked little and stole much.

The farmer was in high anger. He did not say too much when a shovel or a pail was gone, but oilcloth cost much money, and that was different.

He shouted for young Peter his son and said, "Go to the witch doctor and tell him I want to see him. Tell him the fine new oilcloth I bought for covering my wagon is gone. He has helped many a one to find things, and maybe he can help me, too."

Peter was afraid of the witch doctor, so he took along his dog to give him courage. But when they came in sight of the witch doctor's house near the meadow where the black cow was grazing, the dog refused to go. All the coaxing and pulling could not make him go.

So Peter walked alone, very slowly, till he came to the little log house. The black hens were picking grass and grain, and the mistress of the house, short and round as a water barrel, stood in the front of her door. She wore a fine black dress with a silken petticoat, a white silk handkerchief was on her bosom, and a golden brooch hung around her neck.

"Good morning, little Peter," she said, "I'm glad indeed to see you. How is your dear mother and how is your father?"

"They are fine, mistress. I came to see your husband. Our new black oilcloth to cover our wagon was stolen."

"Tze, tze, tze, too bad. But my good husband will find it for you with God's help. He'll find it for you. He always finds things. Come in and tell him all about it. It is noontime, and you can eat with us."

"Oh, no, thank you!" Peter cried. "I must get home."

"I won't let you go until you eat with us," she said, and took him by the hand and pulled him into the house.

Peter saw a sight that frightened him even more. At the long table, there were chairs at each end and six black rocking chairs at each side. In each of these rocking chairs sat a black cat with a nice clean dish and a shining mug before it.

The witch doctor in a black frock coat with a wide ring on his finger sat at the head of the table studying a fat book with large letters. His wife pulled up a chair next to her own at the other end of the table and sat Peter down. Then she filled the fifteen bowls with hot potato soup and poured sweet cool milk in the mugs.

Frightened, Peter said his prayers, and master and mistress did the same. Then all ate, and Peter told of the missing oilcloth.

"I'll come to your father late, quite late, and I will pray for the Lord to help me find the oilcloth. Tell your father to stay in the house and pray."

Peter thanked them both and went out quicker than he had come in and ran home as fast as his little legs would carry him. The dog, sitting on the road, barked joyfully when he saw his master and ran with him.

At home he told his parents what had happened.

The sun had set and the moon stood high when the farmer, watching at the window, saw the little old man in black coming on the road. He carried a cane, and under his arm was a thick book.

He went straight to the barn, opened his book, and began to read aloud. Then he stopped and turned his wrinkled yellow face to the moon and made a large circle around the barn, mumbling words all the time.

Big black clouds rushed up in the sky, there were flashes of lightning and rumbling thunder.

The farmer at the window felt a cold sweat all over, and his hair stood up under his nightcap.

Suddenly a blue-and-red light came over the barn, and wild, fiery shapes in flowing gray shrouds floated through the air. There was a crash loud as a cannon and a fiery wheel came through the air . . . with the black oilcloth floating over it. Wild faces with ragged shrouds hanging down their shoulders flew in from all sides, carrying forks and pails and hoes and harrows which had been missing from the farm. The spirits threw them into the circle the witch doctor had made around the barn.

Maybe they were spirits, maybe Pine Creek folks; the farmer standing frightened at the window couldn't tell.

He saw their mumbling lips and angry faces. Every

time one dropped something into the circle it was with scowls and anger.

Then the wheel rolled away, the spirits disappeared, and the black clouds ran away from the sky. The moon shone softly again, the wind blew gently over the grass, and the witch doctor with the long, yellow teeth walked slowly away.

The farmer ran out and found everything that was ever taken from him, and he was mighty thankful.

He, too, now joined all the folks around Orwigsburg, Pottsville, and other towns in singing the praises of the kind witch doctor of the weird Blue Mountains.

Chug-Chug Along
the O-hi-o

IN THE sweet valley of Sewickley on the banks of the beautiful Ohio in Pennsylvan-i-a many things happened. Some were bold and fearless, some were rib-tickling whoppers that brought good healthy laughter. And since folks need laughter as much as courage, I'll tell of the lollapaloosers with a good ha-ha in them.

One fine day when the sun shone bright on the big river, shone lazy on the green fields and the silent trees, there came along a good hunter of the valley, coonskin cap on his head, a stick in his hand, walking to visit a farmer friend. He stopped to look at the cattle, and then he walked into the barn.

Now it so happened at the same time a very timid little man living in the valley was walking along the selfsame road. He was the kind of man who was scared of a mouse running or of a fly buzzing; he always heard devils and demons in the air.

He saw the hunter's leather shirt with fringes, the coonskin cap with the tail, and he was sure Indians were on the warpath come to kill folks in the sweet Sewickley valley—though at that time there were hardly any Indians left.

He ran back to the village crying the savages were in the valley coming to scalp and kill. He had seen them enter a farmhouse and was sure all were dead there by now.

Men and women, boys and girls caught up whatever they could carry and fled across the Ohio River for escape and for safety. By then the farmer whom the hunter had come a-visiting heard the clatterwhack and ran to see the trouble.

He listened to the tale, laughed, and said they were sillier than the men of Gotham in England, the land from which they had come. So they all returned with silly faces and a little wisdom in their heads.

But wisdom isn't learned in a single day.

Soon new settlers came to the valley. They chose a lovely spot to live and went to sleep under the starry skies to rest for the next day's work.

In the morning when the sun came over the hills, men and boys, big and strong, with ax and hatchet, crowbar and adz, shouting and crying, came to help. But the new settlers thought it was a band of cutthroats come to attack and believed their end was near—until they learned that these were only neighbors to help them build their home.

Men and boys and even women set to work with a good will, and at night the newcomers had a roof over their heads.

But folks follow fear sooner than wisdom.

Came a day when the sharp whistle of the Ohio steamboat was heard for the first time in the sweet valley of Sewickley, and wasn't there a great to-do!

Uncle Sam, the spanglorious steamboat, was chugging along the river with a brand-new whistle the engineer could blow by just touching a valve. That shrill screamer warned vessels and gave every other kind of warning that had to be on a river.

Uncle Sam, kerchugging along, ran aground near the landing, and the captain blew his steamboat whistle shrill and screaming, heard far along the river and deep into the land, for men to come and help him off.

The whistle shrilled and screamed long and strong, and a great fear came over folks in the valley and folks in the hills.

Some said Gabriel was blowing his trumpet and the end of the world had come. They fell on their knees and cried with fear and prayed to the Lord to forgive them their sins and take them into heaven above.

Some folks said the wildcats of the land had come to their valley. They took pitchforks and axes, guns and sticks, to destroy the beasts with the wailing screams.

They ran through fields and they ran through the woods till they came to the Ohio River, and there the river men told 'em the screaming was only the new whistle of the steamboat calling for the help of men.

Some laughed, some growled at their own silliness, but

all lent a helping hand, and soon *Uncle Sam* was chugging proudly along the muddy water.

And the men on the boat and the men on the shore sang together:

> The boatman is a lucky man,
> No one can do as the boatman can.
> The boatmen dance, and the boatmen sing,
> The boatman is up to everything.
> Hi-O-away we go,
> Floating down the river of the O-hi-o.

So folks in the sweet valley of Sewickley along the O-hi-o River worried and helped, laughed and cried, did silly things, and wise ones as well, making that lovely place along the grand river a lovelier place to live in.

The Great Sacrifice

FOLKS in Pennsylvania tell stories of hex and haunt and tales tall as heaven, but they also tell tales of men and places with love and veneration in their hearts. One of these men is George Washington, and one of these places is Valley Forge, where even frozen bodies could not cool the fire of burning freedom.

It is told around fireside and camp that there lived in Valley Forge that winter of the Revolutionary War a man who forgot he fled from Germany to America for freedom's sake.

His name was Manheim, he was a Tory and spied for the English, but his daughter Elizabeth was on the American side. She had a sweetheart on General Washington's staff to whom she told of plots and treachery hatched by Manheim and his friends. In that bitter winter she became ill but kept up her patriotic work just the same.

One fierce, cold winter morning her father learned that General Washington would pass by that very afternoon and might even stop there. Here was a chance to kill the leader of the American War!

Manheim summoned at once some Tories living near, and together they hatched a plan to kill the general.

Elizabeth heard it, but she was too sick to go to camp. She prayed to God to give her the chance to warn Washington when he came.

Manheim and his men waited tensely, playing and drinking. So did Elizabeth, with burning face and parched lips. The day was getting on. A dull and hazy sun shone angrily in the sky, an icy wind whipped the trees and houses, when a lone, tall horseman came down the road. He came to Manheim's house, and the horse slowed down. The rider, General Washington, looked up at the sky, stopped, and knocked at the door.

Manheim watched behind the window.

"It's him," he whispered loudly to the men who were in the side room. "He can't get away this time. Shut the door and wait."

He opened the front door, and a cutting wind rushed in.

"How can I serve you, sir?" said Manheim, smirking. Elizabeth stood behind him.

"May I rest here for a short time and have some feed for my horse?"

"Both, sir, and with pleasure. I'll take your horse to the stable."

"I'll not trouble you, sir," said Washington. "I'll put it up."

The general saw the horse settled comfortably and returned.

"This time we'll catch that big buzzard. I must get him to lie down in my room, and there we'll finish him quickly," Manheim said to his daughter. The girl did not answer. Her throat and her lips were dry, and her eyes burned.

The general was at the door, and Manheim led him into the room next to where the conspirators were.

"Would you like something to eat, sir?"

"No, thanks, all I need is a little rest."

"Then just have a glass of spirits. Elizabeth, fetch the bottle and glasses."

Elizabeth got bottle and glasses, and Manheim filled them and gave one to Washington. He raised his own high and said, "General, here's to success in our undertaking."

"To our success," said the general.

"Now, sir, if you will, you may rest in the upper floor in my room. You can stay as long as you wish. There's a bed there, sir, and you can look upon it as your own. Elizabeth, take the general into my chamber."

They walked into the hall, Manheim holding the candle high and talking all the time, till they came to the head of the stairs.

"Now, Elizabeth, show the general to my room."

Elizabeth began walking up the stairs.

"This way, sir," she said. Her father still stood at the head of the stairs. The girl's head was whirring, she could hardly walk.

"I can't warn him, my father is standing there," the thought kept going round and round in her head. "What shall I do?"

Now she was at the top of the stairs; her father's room

was the first door, her own the second. Without even thinking, she led the general to her own door instead of her father's, opened it, and said low:

"Here, sir, make yourself at home."

General Washington went in and closed the door.

Elizabeth could hardly walk down, and her father saw it.

"Daughter, you are ill, go to your room and lie down, it will do you good."

"I think I will," she said. Her teeth were chattering.

Manheim went into the room where the Tories were waiting. Elizabeth walked up the stairs slowly, stopped for a moment, and then opened the door to her father's room, went in, and lay down on the bed.

All was still.

Manheim was with the two Tories in whispering conversation.

"He's in my room now and shortly will be asleep. We'll throw dice to see who should finish him. No one will look for him till the morrow, and by then we'll be safe with the British and well rewarded."

The dice were thrown and they were against Manheim.

The German did not flinch. "I'll do it," he said. "We'll wait a little to make sure he's asleep."

They sat silent for a time. It was so still in that house you could hear the hearts beat. Outside, the wind screamed in wild fury.

Soon Manheim rose. He took off his boots and walked

slowly up the stairs. It was pitch black, but he knew his way.

The first door was his room; it was there he told Elizabeth to take the general. He had not seen that she had led him into the second door, her own room. . . .

He opened slowly the first door, the door to his room. It was dark there, but he knew well where his bed was and he saw a figure on it. . . . He moved up to it! There was a swift movement in the dark! A moaning cry! . . .

Manheim came down quickly where his men were drinking.

"We must set out at once; it is pretty dark. I'll go fetch Elizabeth."

He ran up again, this time candle in hand. Just as he reached the landing, the door of his daughter's room opened! There stood General Washington!

"Host," he said quietly, "I want to thank you for your hospitality. I must set out. I will see that you are paid by my adjutant." He walked slowly down the steps and out. Manheim stood stock still, unable to speak! Then he rushed into his own chamber and—there was a piercing cry!

The Tory traitors ran up and into the open door; there Manheim stood still as stone and ghostly white, for on the bed lay his daughter, whom he had murdered. She had given her life to save Washington for America.

The Haunted Mine

OXENRYDER came to Pennsylvania, came to the mine patch to mine black, shiny coal, as many a man had done. Some called him Oxenryder, some Oxenreiter, some Hudsonryder, for he came from way up the Hudson. But call him by any name, he was the same oxen-headed unbeliever who cried to all the world there was no God.

He was tall and thin with a hooked nose and coal-black eyes. When he had on his peaked cap with the little flickering oil lamp, and with his black, sooty face and black, shiny, sooty clothes, he looked like the Devil come to the Big Vein colliery, and every man kept out of his way.

Miner folk are God-fearing folk, and they favored no man who said there was no God. But the Big Vein Colliery needed men, so the boss let Godless Oxenryder work.

He lived alone, spoke to no man, and no man spoke to him. Children ran from him, and he hated everyone in that mine patch; said he'd pay them back in kind if ever he had a chance.

On a foggy morning the fireboss who watched for the safety of the workers in the mines told the men not to go down to the shafts, for he smelled gas in the dark, dank gangways.

"Don't go down," the fireboss said. "There's gas down there, an' it would be temptin' God t' go there with a light."

"Ain't scared o' gas, and there ain't no God," said Godless Oxenryder.

"Shouldn't say such words," the fireboss said. "Y'll find out quick 'nuf if there is a God if y' go down the gassy gangways with your lamp."

"I'll go down t' see," said Oxenryder.

Down and down he went, the lighted lamp on his cap. But soon there was a terrible explosion that could be heard far and wide.

The men rushed down and found only pieces of that Godless man! They gathered him into a canvas, put him on an ore-car, and hitched on a mule to pull it up.

"Now at last we're rid o' that Godless fellow," the fireboss said. "He'll never bother us again."

No sooner were the words out of his mouth than there was a wild screaming in the dark gangway, and there was Oxenryder's voice yelling:

"Oxenryder's comin'! Oxenryder's comin'!"

The men were scared white under the black soot and they cried for the mule to go, but the mule shook like a leaf, and all the shouting and beating couldn't make it move an inch.

Another mule was hitched to the car, and that wouldn't budge either.

"The mules, they see the ghost o' that fellow who didn't believe in God, that's why they won't go with that car," the men began to whisper.

A third mule was hitched on, and again there came a ghostly, wild screaming through the black smoky gangways, "Oxenryder's comin'! Oxenryder's comin'!"

The men were frightened, the mule shook all over and wouldn't budge.

"A blind mule wouldn't see the ghost o' that Godless man," said the fireboss. So they took the old mule that had no sight, hitched it to the ore-car that had Godless Oxenryder's pieces, and mule and load went up the slope.

Now, mining folk are true to their kind, through thick and thin and weal and woe, no matter how they be. So the folks of the mine patch said though Oxenryder was a Godless man they'd give 'm a decent man's burial in God's own acre.

They put him in a casket and hired an undertaker to take him to the grave.

The undertaker came with a fancy hearse and two fine white horses. Neighbors were there, so was the priest. But when he was through with the prayer, hoping Oxenryder would go where he'd know there was a God, a wild screaming was heard in the mine patch and through the valley:

"Oxenryder's comin'! Oxenryder's comin'!"

Folks were scared and the horses trembled and frothed at the mouth and wouldn't budge.

"Put that casket on the ash-cart, hitch the blind mule

to 't," an old, old miner said. "It's the only way y'll ever get that Godless body t' God's acre."

So they put the casket on the ash-cart, hitched the blind mule on it, and so took the remains of Oxenryder's body to the turnpike and buried him deep in the earth.

Godless Oxenryder was buried, but his ghost lived on and haunted the mine patch and haunted the Big Vein Colliery.

The fire Oxenryder started in the mine still burnt there, burned down the timbers, burned fiercely so no man could come in. All the water poured on did no good, and in the end the rich mining company and the poor mining folks of the mine patch had to leave that mine haunted by Oxenryder's ghost.

Months and years went by, and on wild and stormy nights you could hear Oxenryder's voice screaming in the Schuylkill Valley:

"Oxenryder's comin'! Oxenryder's comin'!"

Came along another company, which said there were no such thing as ghosts, and they'd sure make that mine work.

They pumped out the water, took out the rusty tracks, put in new timbers and new steel, and asked the men of the valley to come mining in the Big Vein Colliery.

But the men of the valley knew better; they knew Godless Oxenryder was still haunting the mine.

Said the boss of the new company, "I'll show you the mine isn't haunted. I'll put rats into the shafts, those rodents which are always the miners' friends, for they always warn 'em of trouble, an' they'll stay there, as they do in other mines."

They caught hundreds of rats, put 'em in gangways and headings of the mine, but the rats knew that mine was haunted. They found their way out and quickly left the mine.

So the company boss hired men from far away who didn't know it was a haunted mine.

But soon they, too, heard the screaming in the gangways, "Oxenryder's comin'! Oxenryder's comin'!" And they heard it in the valley, too.

There was a flood in the mine, the timbers fell, and not a man could work in it.

The Big Vein Colliery was left again by boss and mining folk, and no mining has ever been done in that mine haunted by Godless Oxenryder.

Three Little Tales
of Washington

IN BEAUTIFUL Washington, in the capital of America that is full of statues, presidents, and senators, folks are no different than in other parts of the land. They are merry and they are sad, they are frightened and they are glad.

Stories told there are made of the same stuff as those told anywhere else in the country, from up Maine clear to California, and now I'll tell you some of them.

Listen.

There lived in the days that are gone, gone not very far, a battling lady in Washington whose name was Anne Royal. She was tall and thin, with an angry face and strong beliefs. And she always carried a green umbrella under her arm.

Folks from the President down were scared of Anne Royal. She printed a newspaper by hand, called it the *Huntress*, and in it scolded and nagged and badgered anyone who did not agree with her. None was safe. Presidents, generals, and senators talked of rigging up an old-fashioned ducking stool in the Navy Yard to duck Anne to keep her quiet.

But that never stopped Anne Royal. She just kept on pestering people to make 'em talk and buy her paper.

One day she could not think of a thing to complain of nor a person to attack, so she decided to write about the President and his politics. She tried to get into the White House to talk to the President, but the guards wouldn't let her in. She stomped along the grand Potomac that was right before the capital in those days, she tried to pass the guards, but it did her little good. The President wouldn't see her.

One hot morning very early, when the sun just peeped over the housetops, the President decided to take a swim in the cool waters of the river that ran right near the White House.

He went down to the water, took off his clothes, and jumped in the moving stream. It was so pleasant and refreshing he never noticed a tall, thin lady with a green umbrella coming toward him.

It was Anne Royal!

She saw the President in the water, saw his pantaloons on the bank, and she knew the President would speak!

She sat down on the pantaloons and cried out sharply, "Good morning, Mr. President."

The President took one look and felt hot in the cooling water.

"I want you to tell me about the troubles between the

U.S.A. and England, and I'll print it in my paper," she said, cool as the running stream.

"Get off my pantaloons," the President cried, "and leave at once so I can come out and have my breakfast."

"I don't get off your pantaloons, and you don't get out of the water for breakfast, until you tell me all the troubles between America and England for my paper."

The sun was rising, and people would be passing soon. A President should not be bathing in the river while ambassadors are waiting to decide who should rule the world. Besides, the President was hungry, just like any other man at this hour in the morning.

The President grumbled and growled and spluttered, but he told Anne Royal all about the troubles in the world.

The lady with the green umbrella went off satisfied, and the President had his breakfast.

Here's a Washington tale that'll bring gladness to your heart.

In those days there stood a wishing tree in Lafayette Square, a little Spanish chestnut tree near the statue of President Jackson on his tall, strong horse. And a real wishing tree it was.

Young and old, white and black, came to that tree and made their wish, and often it was granted.

One fine day pretty Miriam with red-rust hair and violet eyes came to the tree to make a wish.

She didn't wish for a handsome young man but for a

good job in a fancy store to earn enough money to help her father and mother. She made her wish aloud and so earnestly that it was even heard by a rich lady sitting on a bench nearby, a pink silk parasol in her hand. Miriam sat down on the same bench.

"And what was your wish, my pretty maid?" the kind, rich lady said, smiling, though she knew full well what it was.

"Faith, a wish mustn't be told," Miriam said, "or it may never come true."

"Perhaps this time it will come true. Do you want a nice young man or a bright silk dress?"

"None o' these, Ma'am."

"Whatever it is, I am certain your wish made under the wishing tree will be granted," the lady said with a smile.

"I pray the Lord it should come true, for I need it badly."

The lady learned Miriam's name and where she lived.

In a few short days Miriam received a letter which said she was to come to the grand store for the job she had wished for under the wishing tree in Lafayette Square.

Have you ever heard of the Octagon House? The Octagon House in Washington, the weirdest house in the land? There bells ring untouched by hands; heavy, ghostly steps of unseen feet are heard in the dark night on the stairs; women's screams ring through the halls;

chains of slaves rattle and they screech in underground paths.

And for every weird sound there is a harrowing tale.

One day a handsome young officer of a grand British ship went visiting in the Octagon House. The hosts were grand, the company fine, but that young officer had eyes only for a slave girl working in the house, more beautiful than the Rose of Sharon.

The English officer was madly in love with her and even more madly jealous, and one day when she smiled at another man he killed her and hid the body in a closet in one of the chambers of the Octagon House. For three days he stayed in the room with his dead love, and the fourth night he leaped down the grand stairway where others had leaped before, and died. Since then the ghost of that beautiful girl is heard shrieking on moonlight nights, and the handsome young Britisher in full glittering uniform is seen wandering in the room where he committed his crime.

Such are the tales folks tell in Washington, the capital of America.

Clever Jacob Gibson

IN THE years behind our years there lived in the state of Maryland, in the Cockade State, burly Jacob Gibson, and he was as great as any hero who lived in days of old.

Jacob Gibson was a blacksmith, was a planter, was a sailor, was a gentleman, and was a lusty fellow who could outwit a Yankee trader and out-argue a Philadelphia lawyer. He loved a merry prank more than a hundred hogsheads of tobacco and was ever ready for a good fight. He believed:

> Whilst we live we live in clover,
> And when we die we die all over.

His greatest hero was Napoleon, and he thought of him so much that he named his house and possessions after the battles of the great general. But he had a grudge against the British.

Came a time when we had to fight the British on the sea, even as we had to fight them on the land years before. The redcoats raided towns along the coast, destroyed houses, stole cattle, even as they attacked our vessels on the sea. That made Jacob Gibson mad as a hornet, and he swore he'd pay them back for the Americans and for the French as well.

One day part of the British fleet, cruising around Maryland waters, dropped anchor not far from Sharp Island, which belonged to clever Jacob Gibson. They raided the island and put Gibson as well as his men in chains, then took greens and fruit and also twelve fine head of cattle, four sheep, twenty-eight hogs, and sixteen little pigs that were on Jacob Gibson's farm.

Jacob watched them with a smile on his face, humming:

> For every evil under the sun
> There is a remedy or there is none.

Said his overseer who stood next to him, "You don't seem t' mind these robbers robbin' you, Jacob Gibson."

"I'll make 'em pay. I'll make 'em pay. Just you take note," answered Jacob.

The overseer said, "Y' know this is war, Master Gibson, and they make short work o' trouble-makers."

"Oh, I've a smooth tongue, and I mean to make those robbers pay for what they are taking. I'll not get into any trouble."

"You'll make the British pay! You're not as clever as all that, Master Gibson. Watch out, man, or they'll hang y' high as I've heard they are doin' to many others."

"Never fear for me. I've been in worse pickles and found a way out. I can shine when I please, in church and in the drawing room and in the tavern, too. Never fear for me, I'll make of that roaring lion a gentle little lamb."

"Wish y' luck, Master Gibson," the man said.

When the raiding sailors laid hands on Jacob he got talking to them with his honeyed way of speech, and soon, instead of taking him to one of the cruisers, they took off his chains and brought him to the admiral's ship, as he had asked them to do.

No sooner did he get there than he told the sailors an American merchant man desired to speak with Admiral Warren on important private matters.

They led him to the cabin where the admiral sat dressed in gilded braid.

Do you think Jacob Gibson was scared? Not a whit. He spoke up, and in a voice to lure bees from their honey.

Remember, Jacob Gibson could plead harder than a preacher pleading for salvation and could talk a man out of his skin.

Well, Jacob Gibson spoke sugared words, proving in diverse and devious ways, 'pon honor, courtesy, a gentleman's word, and genteel manners which every true-blooded Englishman possessed, that he should be treated like a gentleman. For wasn't he, Jacob Gibson, in a manner of speaking, English, too? His ancestors came from England, he spoke the English language, lived mainly under English laws, dressed like an Englishman, ate like an Englishman. Surely he had the right to claim time-honored English courtesy and consideration!

The admiral listened to the pleasant voice and to the flattering and convincing arguments and really could not say a word against them. In the end the British admiral believed he surely should pay good Jacob Gibson, as fine a gentleman as ever spoke the English language, for the animals taken from him and perhaps make the soldiers apologize for their rudeness.

So Jacob was paid in good English money for his cattle. Then, with friendly toasts and friendly handshaking all around, he was permitted to return to his home.

When Jacob's friends and neighbors heard that he had been paid by the British for the cattle, there was a great hue and cry that Jacob was a traitor. Who ever heard of soldiers or sailors paying for commandeered food! Surely rich Jacob had sold out to the foe! The word spread quickly, and anger ran high. Some were for hanging Jacob, others for putting him in jail. The whole town was against him.

Do you think Jacob Gibson minded this? Not a whit! He was only angry at their blindness. Couldn't they see that a nimble mind could get money even from an enemy? There's more than one way to catch flies.

So he set his mind a-thinking to show his friends and neighbors how silly they were, seeing terror where there was none to see, and that he was as loyal a patriot as any man in Maryland. In the end he thought of a prank fit for any prankster who ever rode through our blessed land and woods or sailed our rich rivers and lakes.

When the night was dark and the clouds rode over the moon, Jacob Gibson took some of his men, boarded his bargelike vessel that had sails and oars, and sailed far out

into the bay. At the first sign of dawn he took a big, red
bandanna kerchief and tied it to the mast. The wind blew
high, and the red flag looked like a British flag waving
gaily in the air. Next he took an empty keg, gave a black
boy a stick, and told him to drum with might and main,
and when he grew tired to have another continue. At no
time was the drumming on the keg to cease. Then he
turned the nose of the boat toward the shore, where
valiant men were on the lookout for the British warships.

No sooner did watchmen on the shore spy the vessel
with the red flag and hear the beating of the drum than
they were certain that an attack was coming their way
by the British.

The alarm was sounded far and wide. Women and
children were rushed to hide in woods and hills; St.
Michaels Patriot Blues came out in arms. Captain Ban-
ning in command called men from all the surrounding
country and armed them with every kind of weapon—
all was ready to give the enemy a hot welcome.

On the waves, green and shimmering from the redden-
ing sky and the rising sun, came Jacob Gibson's boat, red
flag flying and drums beating wildly.

Nearer and nearer up Broad Creek came the craft, and
as it came nearer to St. Michaels the eyes of the watchful
men, guns and sabers, scythes and knives in hand, grew
wider and wider. Soon guns and sabers dropped! All
stood rooted to the ground!

That was Jacob Gibson's boat! And Jacob Gibson's

black boy was beating on the drum, whistling "Yankee Doodle Came to Town!"

Jacob moored his boat and came smiling ashore, never saying a word. Men leaped in wild anger upon him, and for the moment it seemed his end had come. Some shouted for tarring and feathering; some for hanging. Then Jacob Gibson raised his voice and said:

"Hang me? For what? Fools! Blind moles! First you want to hang me for outwitting the British and call me a traitor! Now you'd hang me for a jest to show you how blind anger can blind man's reason. There was as much reason thinking me a traitor for making the enemy pay for my cattle as there is for thinking my boat an enemy boat because I was beating on a hogshead and tied a red kerchief on to my mast."

Well, the crowd was angry for being fooled, but still they had to laugh for being frightened at a red bandanna kerchief and a hogshead drum. So it all ended in a good laugh.

No one ever accused clever Jacob Gibson again of betraying his country. Instead, they listened to his counsel and used his clever tongue and smart head whenever there was need to.

A Merry Tale of Rich Neck Farm

WHEN lovely ladies had beauty patches, and men wore silken hose, there were many gay parties in the homes and manor houses of Maryland. At these parties old and young, black and white, were so gay and happy you would think all trouble had gone from the world.

Once there was such a gay party on Rich Neck Farm along the Eastern Shore. Black fiddlers played violins, a grand company dressed in silks and satins danced, and fine food and cooling drinks were served under gleaming chandeliers and twinkling stars. All were as merry as merry could be except a few young ones, boys and girls of the house and their friends, who had been told they could not stay up as long as their elders because they were too young. When did young people like to be called too young to stay up!

It made them angry as ruffled roosters. They were young but full of life and maybe could stay up all night much better than those who were as old as twenty-five or maybe even thirty-five. But parents' words were law and had to be obeyed.

The nearer the hour came when Miss Emma and Miss Grace, and Samuel, Matthew, and James had to leave, the more angry they were. The party was so lovely and exciting! Fiddlers played in the ballroom, little crickets fiddled around the lawn, and fireflies and guests danced to their hearts' content. Even the moonlit water all around the "point" that could be seen through great leafy trees and giant needle pines were dancing a swelling, shimmering dance all their own. There really was no reason in all the world why one should leave such pleasure and sights just because the clock would strike eleven.

All five stood together a little way from the lawn. Said Samuel:

"I just can't see any reason at all why we have to go to our rooms when everybody is having the grandest time here."

"No, brother," Emma said, "it's not fair, and I just hate to do it. I've argued and begged Mother, and she said we have to obey."

"I'm not going to," said Samuel. "I'm not going to do it, it's not fair and I've an idea. Let's have a party all by ourselves as late as we want and as early in the morning as we want."

"How are we going to have a party all by ourselves?" asked Emma.

"I'll tell you how. Let's get cake, sweet persimmon wine, and fruit and hide 'em, then instead of going to bed we five will stay up and have a good time by ourselves."

"It's a great idea," said James.

"Where? Surely not in the house." This from Matthew.

"No, silly, of course not in the house. I'll hide all the things behind a stone in the cemetery. Then, instead of going to our rooms, we'll go there and have a fine time eating and drinking and telling tales."

All agreed it was a wonderful scheme.

Samuel and his sister Emma packed a basket full of sweets, cakes, and sweet wine, and, unseen by anyone, took it to the little family cemetery that was near the house.

You must know that down in Maryland the family cemetery was often right near the house, and no one was afraid to go there any time, day or night.

In the cemetery the two put the basket with the food and bottles behind one of the stones and then went back to the gaily lit house, to their friends.

Now, it so happened that on that very day three young Negro boys had gone on an errand to Clairborn and were right about that time on their way home.

The eldest of the three, Abe, had a lighted lantern in his hand, though the moon shone full. He and the other two were talking about this and that just to hear their voices and keep fear from their minds.

Suddenly they heard a grunting, the kind a wild hog makes. There were many of these wild hogs roaming in the woods in those days, and poor black and white folks would catch them for a little feast, and masters would just not notice it.

"Lord a-mercy, it's a gray spirit!" cried Cato, shivering with fright. He was the youngest of the three.

" 'Tain't no ghost 't all. It's a wild hog, an' you's plum empty-headed not t' know that," said Abe. "It's a wild hog an' nothin' else. If we is smart we kin catch 't an' have a gran' pa'ty jus' the same as Massa in the big house."

"Mah mouf's full o' water," said James, who walked on the other side of Cato. "Come, let's catch 'm quick."

The three, never thinking of their fear, walked carefully, following the noise.

The grunting and squealing grew louder, as if the animal were in pain. Soon they came on a young wild hog caught under the branches of a fallen maple.

Abe and the others threw themselves on the pig and held it tight. Then they tied its legs the best they could, and Abe, who was the strongest, threw it over his shoulder, and they all turned homeward.

When they came near the house, they heard the music and the voices and saw they'd have to be seen passing with the pig, for their quarters were in back of the main house. They all stopped. Said Abe:

"We jest can't go past with all them lights."

"No we cain't," said James ruefully.

"Guess we got t' hide that pig," said Cato.

"That's jest what Ah'm goin' do. Ah'll hide that pig in the buryin' groun' where no one's sure t' come. And when all the guests 's gone we come an' git it."

"Ain't you scared o' ghosts?"

"There is no ghosts in Massa's cemetery, on'y in black fo'ks's."

"You's always got a smart haid," said James.

So Abe, followed by the two, went quietly into the cemetery that was surrounded by giant trees and carefully laid down the tied pig behind a stone, not far from where Samuel and Emma had put the basket for the party. Abe never saw it. Then he and the other two went to their quarters.

Now hogs sleep at night just as people do, and this little wild hog, all tuckered out from excitement, went to sleep peacefully behind the tombstone.

The moon was riding high in the star-filled sky when Miss Emma and Miss Grace, led by Samuel, Matthew, and James, came quietly down the rear stairway. They walked carefully in back of the house in a wide circle so as not to be seen by the jesting, laughing company, then down behind the trees outside of the lawn, and so to the cemetery, where they let themselves through the gate.

All five were in gay spirits, for this was high adventure.

"I hope some of your ancestors come to life and join us," said James jestingly.

A black cat ran across their path. Samuel stopped.

"That's a bad sign," he said. "Maybe it was a ghost."

"I'm not afraid of ghosts. Come, I've been around all the years and I've never seen a ghost," said Matthew.

"I'd like to see a ghost once," said Emma, giggling.

"I just love this kind of a party," said Grace. "It feels nice and kind o' curly down my spine."

So jesting, they went between the stones, Matthew in front.

Suddenly he stopped dead! And the others did the same behind him.

They all heard a queer kind of snoring, almost right in front of them!

"Lord! what's that?" said Grace, with a little quiver in her voice.

Maybe the hog heard the voice, or maybe it woke up suddenly. Whichever it was, it was wide awake and in panicky fright. It began squealing and squawking and rolling fiercely and got out of the rope and rags wound around its legs. Freed, it began running wildly to get away. First it hit the basket that held the food and bottles and threw it over, breaking the bottles with a crash loud as thunder—or so it seemed to the five standing there rooted to the ground, not knowing just what was running and what was happening.

Then the pig raced wildly around the stones, squealing and grunting, as if it were in scalded water.

Now, you know unknown noises in the night, particularly if you have a guilty conscience or fear in your heart, sound a thousand times louder than they are. The crash of bottles, the screeching and squealing, the swishing and rushing around in the darkness of something you could not see clearly made noises louder than the trumpets of Jericho and more frightening.

"It's the Devil," screamed Emma, and began to run. The others followed, just as scared, and they never stopped until they reached the manor house, where the hosts and guests were still having a grand time.

The tale of the Devil hid behind the tombstone was soon told, and some laughed and others cried for lanterns, and soon all the company trooped into the little cemetery.

The broken bottles were found, and food, and some even saw hoofmarks.

Some believed the tale of the Devil, some that an animal had scared them; only Abe, Cato, and James knew the truth, and they didn't tell right then. So Miss Emma, Miss Grace, Samuel and Matthew and James really believed the Evil One had come to punish them for disobeying, and they were mighty careful about what they did from then on.

That's one way to learn not to do things you shouldn't.

Romance at Tulip Hill

ON TULIP HILL, in rippling Maryland, stands a lordly house with beautiful terraced gardens filled with marching romance, lovely dreams, and dark deeds fit for tale and song.

One night a gay young cavalier came home late to Tulip Hill, where the white stairway is wide enough for horses to ride abreast, chambers are spacious enough for state affairs, and ceilings high enough for birds to fly. The hour was late, but he would bid good night to his mother just the same. So he rode up the stairs on his noble steed right into his mother's chamber, and there he bade her a sweet good night. You can see the hoofmarks on the stairway to this very day.

One time in Tulip Hill there was a bleak underground passage to the river, with wet, dripping stones where slaves were dragged from stinking shipholds and inhuman deeds were done.

And once there happened in Tulip Hill a romance sweet enough to please any maid in Maryland, or in all the world.

That was in the days when young Miss Elizabeth was mistress of Tulip Hill house.

She was fresh as a rose, pretty as a bird, and as good as any Quaker maid could be. She never missed a "meeting," and dressed in Quaker garb, which became her very well, and she never raised her voice to friend or slave. In fact, she had all the virtues a Quaker or any maid should have.

Now, there lived a nice young man not far from Tulip Hill; his name was Thomas Sprig. He was a gay young cavalier, who could ride as well as any man in Maryland, play as long as any man, and work as hard as any man.

One day he saw sweet young Elizabeth, and from then on her soft eyes and pretty face were a light guiding him to Tulip Hill house, even as the giant tulip trees guided sailors, sailing along the Patuxet River.

He forgot to eat or drink, play or ride, thinking all the time of lovely Elizabeth sitting there in the loveliest terraced garden in all Maryland.

He was always finding reasons to visit the fine brick house, and always on such visits he found a way to walk with young Elizabeth along the garden paths lined with sharp-smelling boxwood and holly and scented guelder-roses. Elizabeth seemed to favor these walks with Thomas amid the green and flowers, talking of this and that and everything young people talk about.

One day they sat together in a bower with the sweet smell of lavender and basil all around them. The sun shone brightly, the wind blew gaily, and birds were singing all around. It was so happy a day that Thomas found the courage to ask Elizabeth if she loved him and would wed him.

Elizabeth looked first at the flowers, then into Thomas's eyes, then she spoke:

"Love thee I do." Then she was silent for a time, looking at the gentle violets and lady's-slippers growing along the path. "Love thee I do, Thomas," she spoke again, "but marry thee I cannot."

"And why not?" asked Thomas in surprise.

"I can't marry thee, for thee are a worldling and a wastrel. Friends do not marry such men. And, besides, I would never marry a man who is not a Friend."

Tom pleaded and begged, but it helped him little with Elizabeth, who was lovely and demure but very determined. She said she would never marry a man who played cards and did many things that were shocking to a Quaker maid.

Tom left in great anger, only to return a few days later to renew his pleading, but it did him little good. Elizabeth was that steadfast.

This kept on for some time. One day he pleaded longer than usual, and with the deepest fervor. Finally Elizabeth said she would marry him if he became a Friend, went to meeting, worshiping and living the honest Friends' way.

This put Tom in great anger, for he could see no reason why any man should give in to a maid's stubbornness. He lost his temper and told Elizabeth in sharp words that she was a silly person. In the end Tom whipped the trees

with his riding whip, shouting, "I'm going, and I swear
I'll never set foot nor eye on Tulip Hill again, nor on
your stubborn, silly face."

Elizabeth was not long in answering quietly: "Wait
till I invite thee. Thee will wait a long time indeed."

Young Tom rushed away without another word, slam-
ming the gate as hard as he could. As for Elizabeth, she
walked up the terraces toward the house, head high in
the air and eyes wide open, never noting the velvety
heartsease nor any other flowers along the path.

From that day on Thomas Sprig rode harder, played
more, and drank more than any man in Talbot County.
But there was no pleasure for him in the riding or the
playing or the drinking or in anything. Day and night
pretty Elizabeth was on his mind and in his heart, and,
try as he would, he could not get her out.

When on the hunt or with boon companions, Elizabeth's sweet face and quiet voice were ever there, and
he was always hearing the words of how she would
marry him.

Soon he was no longer gay as he used to be. He would
neither ride nor join in games, and he began to see less
and less of his friends.

And where do you think Thomas Sprig was? He was
visiting Friends to inquire of their ways of life.

The more he learned, the less he was afeared of it.

They were simple people who did not dress in braids
and gold. They lived a simple life, yet they seemed contented.

Soon he began to think that it was not so very bad to be a Friend and marry Elizabeth, whom he loved more than anyone in the world, and without whom life seemed not worth living. Then he made a great resolve but never said a word to kith nor kin about it.

Again one day, a day lovely as days in Paradise, Tom came to Tulip Hill. The birds and the sun and the wind were singing in grand chorus, and every leaf and flower was swaying in the happy song of life. Everything was gay save young Elizabeth sitting on the very last terrace in the garden, overlooking the river. Her head was bent low, looking at the flowers and at the river but not seeing them. She had been that way from the day young Tom ran away in anger at her words, though she would deny this if anyone told her that. But way down in her heart she was unhappy for what she had said. But Elizabeth was strong-willed and never would own up to herself, or to anyone else, that she was sorry.

She sat a long time or a short time, I can't tell. Suddenly she heard coming down the green terraces steps she thought she recognized. Her face became crimson, and her heart beat loud and fast. She looked up, and there before her stood young Tom.

At first glance she wasn't sure it was he. He wore no gold braid or colored breeches; he wore no gay cockaded hat on his head, nor did he carry a fancy riding whip in his hand. Instead, he was dressed all in brown, the kind of clothes that Friends wore.

For a time she looked at him and he looked at her, and neither spoke a word. Then Elizabeth said:

"Thee are here!"

"So I am. I came to ask thee to keep the promise thee gave me."

He even spoke the Friends' way.

"I see thee are in Friends' dress," Elizabeth said.

"And I go to Friends' meetings—nay, I am a Friend, too, and now, when are we to wed? I hope a Quaker maid will keep her word."

He looked full in Elizabeth's eyes, which now shone glimmering moist.

Elizabeth smiled sweetly and then she spoke low:

"I've made a promise and I'll keep it, Tom."

"Then we be promised to marry!" cried Tom.

"We be promised to marry," Elizabeth whispered.

Married they were in the Friends' way, and they lived happily ever after.

And this is a romance of Tulip Hill house, and a lovely romance it is.

Cookus, Bopple, and Yeakle

DO YOU want to hear about three friends in Hagerstown in lovely Maryland who were wise 's a pea hid safe in a pod and happy 's a bird on the wing? If you do, then listen to a mighty fine story.

Well, there lived three wise friends in Hagerstown who were nearly always together. In rain or shine, in heat or cold, you'd be pretty sure to see 'em in one and the same place, making chin music to beat swallows flying, and laughing at men working day and night to get rich in a hurry. These three were content with what they had, and they had a grand time having it.

Just because of that, folks in Hagerstown said they were queer—just as queer as their names. And, to be sure, their names were queer.

One was called Cookus, the other Yeakle, and the third Bopple. Cookus, he was the biggest, fattest man in Hagerstown, and the easiest-going as well. He got him a pair of fine game cocks, the finest far and wide. Any time he needed money, he'd challenge some other man who had game cocks and win enough money to last him heaps of days.

Yeakle, who was a tinsmith, loved horses to ride and horses to pet more than making hammer music on white tin. He never worked more than he had to. Just enough for good feed for his horses and enough for himself to get by.

Each time his friend Cookus would challenge someone for a cock fight Yeakle 'd pick up a horse race and both 'd win sure as the Lord made little lambs.

Bopple, the third of these three, spoke loud and fast as a mill. He had a wagon and a team of horses he wouldn't change for the crown of France. They were fast and steady and strong, and they had little, jingling silver bells around their necks that made sweet music on the roads. Bopple rode around the town, a big smile on his round face, carrying things and presents for folks, but he never made more money than he had to, so's to spend more time with Cookus and Yeakle.

But the people of Hagerstown shook their heads and pitied him.

One Sunday—it was really Monday, for it was early in the morning—just before sunrise, there was a great shouting and a hubbub and crying in the streets of the town. All the good folks, young and old, ran out to see if a house were on fire or the Indians were attacking with tomahawks. Cookus, Bopple, and Yeakle were there, too. Everyone was babbling and jawing to beat bobtail, about how the Devil had got locked up in the brick church and was howling and yelping like the day of doom.

The sexton came on the run and slowly opened the big door with his big key.

Soon as the doors were open, there shot out a yelping, barking, big black dog, looking even bigger and blacker because it was still dark in the sky and people were mighty scared. That black critter flew out of the doors to beat creations and was gone like the wind.

"That sure was the Devil with black wings," screamed a woman in the crowd.

"An' he had a cloven foot and leaped clean o'er our heads," said another.

"Ah declare t' graciousness, he sure leaped o'er twenty haids," said a Negro man with curly hair.

So each and every one flung language around about the Devil and witches high and wide like hail on a windy day. Soon near every mother's child was certain sure it was the Devil himself they had seen, when it really was only a big black dog.

The animal had come to the house of God during the day and fallen asleep under a pew and couldn't get out because the sexton had locked the doors tight.

Said Yeakle to Cookus, "Wonder what ails folks? Didn't they see with their own eyes that it was only a dog with black hair?"

"People kin scarcely see the nose in the middle of their face," said Bopple, "and then they see only the tip o' that."

"Ho, ho, ho," laughed Cookus. "That's a good 'un.

They see on'y the tip o' their nose!" He laughed till his sides ached.

That got people mad, for they don't like to see a body laugh when they are scared. They told the three to run along—maybe follow the Devil just gone.

So the three friends went their own way, telling each other there was nothing more blind and silly than silly blind folks.

That morning there was again a big to-do in the town that set tongues wagging. Only this time it wasn't about the Devil but about politics.

The post-office man of Hagerstown died sudden-like after running to see the Devil in the church that night, and now they had to get a new post-office man.

Cookus, Bopple, and Yeakle were sitting in Stone's Tavern on Potomac Street drinking yellow cider, and there was great disputing who'd be the next post-office man.

Arguing and speeching came like a waterfall.

In the end a few who wanted the job said they'd go themselves or send someone for them to the great capital Washington to ask to be post-office man of Hagerstown.

Now among those was one called Schnebly. He was a smart one and figured it'd be quicker to send Yeakle on his best-leggenest horse to Washington than to go himself asking for the job.

They got together, a price was set, and Yeakle mounted his finest mare and set out to bring Schnebly the right to be post-office man in Hagerstown.

Another fellow who wanted the same asked Bopple to drive hard to Washington for the same thing; still another gave Cookus a horse and told him to go and get him the post-office job, and two others went themselves on horseback.

They started all together, eating up ground like a rabbit on the run. But after racing for a time they kind of eased up, and there was the whole string of 'em spread over the road. Cookus was the very last one of that string.

Soon he sat down by the wayside and said to himself: "I've run till I've lost my breath so I can't find it no more. That fellow who tol' me to race post haste t' Washington t' get him the post-office job is better off 'tendin' his own work. No man kin do two jobs—one's a-plenty. So I'll jest rest my bones and let the others hog the miles."

He rested a good while, then he went on behind the others till he came to a wild stream swollen with rain. Bopple, Yeakle, and all were there, trying to figure how to get over. There was a ferry, but it had already left shore, and it was loaded with oxen and carts.

All hollered for the ferryman to come back, for they were in a hurry, but that ferryman just kept on going his way. They could do nothing except cool their heels.

All except Yeakle. He plunged his horse in that churning water like a flying fish and was quick enough on the other side on his way to Washington the great capital.

He was there before all the others and got the post-office job for Schnebly, who had sent him to get it. Then he set racing homeward.

On the way he met the others, and they turned, too, so they all came back together to Hagerstown.

Again there was heaps of language flying around like swallows feeding the young, and there was a great celebration, too.

When Yeakle got his money from Postmaster Schnebly for bringing him the job, he and his friends Cookus and Bopple came to Stone's Tavern to celebrate and toast the fine horse that brought the gold.

In the tavern Yeakle sat with more proudness than a lady dressed for a ball, telling everybody how he won that race for the post-office master's job. When he had told it for about the twentieth time, or maybe more, Cookus made a face, snorted, and roared:

"Friend Yeakle, I boun' you fair et up that road with that horse o' yours, like the jay bird carryin' wood on Friday for the Devil."

"Guess I went pretty fast," said Yeakle.

"An' I ambled along. An' so did friend Bopple," said Cookus, keeping on making faces and snorting.

"So I did, so I did," said Bopple over and over again.

"Guess you did, the two o' you," said Yeakle, humble-like, as if he were feeling pity for his friends.

"Well," said Cookus, "we all three, the fast one and slow ones alike, is sittin' here an' havin' fun alike, ain't we?"

"That's right," said Yeakle.

"You worked till salty sweat ran down your horse's sides, an' maybe yours, too," said Cookus again.

"That's a fac', that's a fac'," said Yeakle.

"And Bopple an' me didn't work with salt sweat runnin' down our backs, did we, Yeakle?"

"Guess you didn't."

"Well," said Cookus slowly, his wet face shining, "you eat an' drink same as we do an' no more, don't you?"

"Guess I do!"

"So you see, friend Yeakle," said Cookus, "them that slaves workin' don' get more'n them that don't."

"Guess you're right, Cookus," said Yeakle with a smile, for he saw what his friend was aiming for.

"Well, then," said Cookus, "put your pride in your deep pocket, for it's past endurin', an' just remember, beatin' a man in a race don' make you better nuf' to look down on others. Pride often comes before fallin', as the Good Book tells us."

"Cookus," cried Yeakle, "you're right. Maybe I did let pride get the best o' me, but I'm not goin' t' fall so long 's you is my friend, Cookus, an' kin watch over me."

And from that day the three were even better friends than they were before—the three wise friends of Hagerstown: Cookus, Bopple, and Yeakle.

The White Mule Ghost

WAY back yonder in Tobacco Stick there was a mule all white wi' just a couple o' gray hairs you'd never see except if you'd look mighty close.

Now, everybody knows right well a mule's half a horse, an' near everybody knows what folks say 'bout a white horse:

> One white foot you buy 'm,
> Two white foots you try 'm.
> White all over an' a white nose,
> Cut off his head an' throw him to the crows.

Y' could've said them words 'bout the white mule I'm tellin' y' 'bout. It had green-glassy eyes, an' 'twas the stubborn'st mule ever lived in all Maryland. Maybe in all the states of America.

'Twouldn't plow, 'twouldn't harrow. Y' couldn't ride it, y' couldn't hitch it. 'Twouldn't walk, 'twouldn't run, an y' couldn't even make it eat or drink unless it had a mind t'.

Black folks said a devil was sittin' inside o' that mule's white hide an' would come out only if the mule 'd do a good deed. That's what black folks said.

Now, the boss man who owned that white mule was just 's stubborn as the mule. The more stubborn the mule was 'bout doin' things, the more stubborn the man was to make it do 'em. Them two never got no place.

One day the boss sent Samson, his big black man, t' put some sense into that mule's head—make it same 's other mules.

Sam was the biggest black man 'round Dorchester County, an' he wasn't scared o' nothin' walkin' or flyin'. He took a rope in his hand, walked to the horse lot where the white mule was pasturin', studyin' what t' do. Suddenly a big black cat ran acrosst 'm on the road.

Big Sam didn't like this nohow, for he was a smart fellow and knew that meant a disappointment. He shook his head an' walked on, studyin' more what t' do till he got in the horse lot. There was that white mule on all its four legs starin' with its green-glassy eyes straight at Samson's black eyes. Samson, he stopped, for he saw there was a mighty mean look in that animal's eyes, like it guessed right smart what the black man was after.

Well, Sam he walked kind o' slowly t' the mule, swingin' the rope as if he was swingin' it just for fun. He was gettin' nearer t' the mule lookin' at 'm with the green-glassy eyes.

Samson took a few steps, an' the mule shook its head warnin'-like. But the black man kept edgin' nearer. When the beast saw Samson wouldn't take no warnin', it made a funny noise, openin' its mouth an' showin' its teeth, then it raised its head high an' began stretchin' its hind legs.

Black man 'd never seen a mule stretchin' its legs, an' I didn't neither. But that white mule did it just the same, stretchin' its legs, stretchin', stretchin' its back legs foot after foot. Samson stood watchin', his eyes poppin' out o' his head like a toad frog. He couldn't move nohow.

The mule, it kept on stretchin' those legs pretty near twenty feet, maybe thirty, which proved sure certain the Devil was sittin' inside of its white hide helpin' it in such unnatural business.

Soon the white legs came up right near where Samson was standin' nailed to the green grass. And when those stretchin' legs got near the great big black man they raised 'mselves an' give 'm a mighty kick that sent 'm flyin' half across the length o' the lot. Then it ran away to graze.

Samson lay a long time in the grass till his master come runnin' to find out.

Big Samson got up, his back an' bones full of aches 'n pains.

"Massa," says he, "that mule has the Devil sittin' in his inners. Maybe it's the Devil hisself. When I got in the lot it begin stretchin' its hind legs longer an' longer an' longer till it got near me, then them hoofs gave me a kick sent me clear t' Jerusalem. No man kin tame that white mule till the Devil inside o' him gits out. That's what old Josephine says. She says the Devil, he kin only git out if that mule does somethin' good. Didn't believe her but now I do. I fools no longer wi' that mule."

That made the man even more stubborn t' break the mule of its stubbornness.

He studied a long time 'bout it, then he called black Samson again and said, "Now we're goin' build a fence 'round that mule, an' when we get it inside we'll knock a little sense in its head."

So they built a fence high an' strong round the lot where the mule was grazin'.

The mule watched the doin's from the corner of its green-glassy eyes and didn't do nothin'.

When the fence was done the man said, "Tomorrow I'll teach that mule t' behave like any mule in Maryland."

The next mornin' the man an' Samson went to the pen, opened the gate an' . . . there wasn't no mule.

In the night when the wind blew hard and the clouds flew fast, the mule, with the Devil's help, stretched its four legs long 'nuf to leap over that high fence easier than rollin' off a pea.

From that day on, white mule wasn't seen except at night.

Men comin' on lonesome roads or through the marshes 'd see the mule gallopin' an' thunderin' along in the moonlight lookin' like a white four-footed ghost with green-glassy eyes. 'Twas enough to scare roarin' lions in the wilderness.

Once a strong man tried t' catch it, but 'twasn't no use. Everybody, black folks an' white folks, was sure the Devil was inside o' that mule helpin' it 'gainst man an' beast.

But the man that owned the beast wouldn't give up.

Said he'd catch it and make it a good mule if it took 'm till Judgment Day.

One day he asked all the folks around Tobacco Stick an' nearby t' come an' help 'm catch it. Everybody came with ropes an' halters, sticks an' whips to catch the white mule o' the marshes.

All day long an' all evenin' long they beat the woods an' bushes lookin' for the beast. Then when a small silver-blue moon shone over the trees they spied it right in the middle o' the marsh.

Men an' boys spread out round the marsh an' then began closin' in on the animal, closin' in nearer an' nearer till they got it in the corner goin' into a creek an' swamp full o' quicksand. Men an' boys with sticks an' whips kept on comin' nearer an' closer. At the head was the man who owned the mule an' his black man Samson, a big rope in his hand.

The mule had fire in its green-glassy eyes, the man who owned it had triumph in his. This time he was goin' catch that mule. But he figured too quick.

Just when everybody was close round the animal an' it'd have to be catched or have t' jump in the quicksand to be swallowed up sure, it took one more angry look at the man an' Sam an' leaped right in the quicksand.

First the white legs went down in the movin' sand, then the rest of it, an' in the end the head with the green eyes starin' defiance at everybody all 'round.

Then the white mule was no more.

That's what everybody in Tobacco Stick thought, an'

they was mighty glad to be rid o' the stubbornest mule in Maryland. But they was wrong. They wasn't rid o' that white mule yet. It still was there certain, an' there was trouble then if there never was before.

Now it was a reg'lar ghost mule without any peace at all till it had done some good deed, black folks said.

That's the agreement it had with the Devil for lettin' no man put a halter round its neck. It was now a ghost mule in the swamps an' marshes round 'bout Tobacco Stick.

In the dark night it rushed through woods an' scrub, scarin' man an' beast, even creepin' things. It sure was tormented by the Devil for sellin' its soul.

For a time folks was scared to set foot at night outdoors round those parts. Only those who had a bad conscience or out t' do somethin' they hadn't ought t' do came out on the dark roads along the marshes, an' one o' those bad uns was Bill Chase.

Bill was big 's an oak with even a bigger thirst. Never did a lick of honest work, lazyin' round an' fishin' just 'nuf t' eat. Didn't believe in anythin', not even the white ghost mule. Nights he spent in taverns idlin' the time away with too many rum-dums.

Preacher tried t' make 'm good, but Bill Chase wouldn't be good. Folks tried to make 'm good, but Bill Chase wouldn't be good. Wife tried to make 'm good, but Bill Chase wouldn't be good. No, not he, he just wouldn't be good.

One night, the fall o' the year when the wind howled wild an' the blue moon battled with the black clouds for

a chance to peep through, Bill Chase was amblin' home
along the path through the woods, not too sure on his
feet. He lost his way but didn't care. He came t' a spot
that had a kind o' marshy clearin', an' there he stopped,
dead-like. His hair stood up straight as porcupine quills.

The moon tore a big rift in the clouds an' was shinin'
full on the murky, marshy, sandy clearin', an' on the
white head of the mule risin' slowly from the sand. The
green-glassy eyes were starin' at 'm as the body o' the
ghostly beast came higher an' higher till it stood there
on its four white legs—solid on the quicksand!

Bill Chase, he shook like an aspen leaf. His throat was
dry, an' he couldn't swallow. He tried t' lift his legs, but
they was heavy as rocks. He took one step, stumbled, an'
fell on his face. Up he got an' tried again but fell again
on the grass. He got up and didn't try to run no more, he
just stood lookin' at the glassy eyes o' the mule starin'
at him, pleadin'-like an' beggin'. So they stood lookin' at
each other for a time, then the white ghost mule, it began
sinkin' back in the quicksand as if it had done told a
message to Bill Chase what it had come t' tell.

Well, Bill Chase, he lit out like there was fire under
his feet. He ran an' ran. He was green-scared, thinking
how he'd seen a ghost stumblin' an' fallin', a sure sign he'd
have the worst luck in the world from now on.

When he got home he wouldn't tell wife nor child
what happened. He just sat down, waited for the bad
luck t' come, as it always did when you see a fallin' ghost
an' you falls yourself.

He waited one day, another, an' another, never doin' a lick o' work, expectin' trouble. No trouble came.

He waited some more, waited for trouble. But no trouble came—not even trouble o' worryin' 'bout money for bacon or sugar. For since he didn't spend his money in the tavern there was 'nuf to buy things needed.

That set him a-thinkin'. No trouble comin', no worry 'bout vittles, an' all thanks to the ghost mule that looked at 'm with sad green-glassy eyes an' stumbled. All thanks to that poor, tormented beast that had the Devil in its white hide. Maybe some day he, too, 'd be tormented, for he, too, was followin' the Devil the way he acted, just like the white mule. That's what preacher said.

Then a great fear fell on Bill Chase. He was sure certain he'd be tormented if he didn't mend his ways, walk in the ways o' God as preacher, neighbors, an' his wife wanted him to. Bill Chase became a different man.

He walked in the ways o' the Lord instead o' the ways o' the Devil. Went to church, worked hard, and wasn't seen no more in the tavern. Next he turned preacher an' was famous far an' wide. An' he always told how the white mule ghost had made a good man o' him, an' folks said it was a miracle.

The white ghost mule was never seen no more after that. The Devil left it, and it rested in peace.

So the mule saved Bill Chase, an' Bill Chase saved the mule, which is the way things happen down here in Maryland.

God's Well

IN THE young, green years of our land there was once a dry, brown summer in Maryland, in Talbot County. For weeks there was no rain and it was hot and windy. Flowers bent weakly, and there were no red fruits; cattle were bony with thirst, birds with hanging wings hopped about only now and then, mouths wide open, and grass was scorched from the baking heat.

Brooks stopped flowing, and the still waters in the lakes were low. So low you could wade in them. Everyone suffered, and folks prayed to God for rain.

In the towns, people suffered, too. Those whose springs had not dried up put locks on their pumps so no neighbor could get a drop of their precious water. That is the way people often are, and they were no different in the little town of Westminster.

In that town there lived two ladies, Miss Lydia and Miss Betsy, who were kind and God-fearing women. They went to the holy church, where they prayed not only with their lips but with their hearts as well. They were Christians who did what the Lord wants folks to do.

Old Miss Lydia and old Miss Betsy lived in the home of their father, who was one of those who founded Westminster. In back of the house there was a spring that gave the finest water in the land; it was sweet and fresh and sparkling like a May morning.

That summer all the springs of the town were getting lower and lower, and some had dried up altogether, but not the spring of Miss Lydia and Miss Betsy. That was full as ever.

In a short time there was but one spring with water besides the one which belonged to the old sisters. A man owned that spring, and he watched it night and day so no one but himself would get a drop of precious liquid. Fear, desperation, and anger filled men's hearts and made them mean and hard.

Said Miss Betsy to Miss Lydia:

"Lydia, why are people so hardhearted? Those who still have water will not give a drop to those who have not. They put locks on their pumps and drive the thirsty away."

"Sister," answered Miss Betsy, "I don't know the ways of man, but I know the ways of God, and He teaches us that we are brothers and sisters and should help each other. That is what the Bible tells us to do."

"Then we will do accordingly," said Miss Lydia. "We will take a wooden board and put on it an invitation for everyone to come and take all the water they need."

The word was said and the deed was done. They got a large wooden plank and painted on it in large letters:

FREE ADMITTANCE TO ALL

WATER BELONGS TO GOD

This sign they put high over the gate of their house, and they left the gate wide open. By then there was not a single spring of water left in Westminster except Miss Lydia's and Miss Betsy's. Soon folks in town and folks living nearby came to the spring of the two maiden sisters and took the life-giving water they needed.

Folks traveling to the great West read the sign at the gate. They stopped to refresh themselves and their beasts and went their way, with a prayer of thankfulness to God for such good people.

More and more took water from God's Well, as the spring was now called, and the more water taken the more water it had. Folks said it was a miracle such as happened in the days of the Lord! For water from God's Well gave water to the multitude.

Now, during all this time men, women, and children prayed Sundays and every day for rain to come.

Miss Lydia and Miss Betsy prayed as well. They prayed not for themselves but for others.

One evening Miss Lydia said to Miss Betsy, "There's a mackerel sky on high. Perhaps God will bless us with rain."

Late at night Miss Betsy said, "See, there's a mare's tail in the sky. I truly think you're right."

A strong wind blew from the east, and there was a ring around the moon.

Soon the sky was covered with dark clouds. There came thunder and lightning and blessed rain fell in waterfalls on the dry, dusty earth and on the suffering people and animals.

It rained for days, as if to make up for lost time. It rained so long everyone had enough water for their needs.

But folks never forgot God's Well that never went dry and how good Miss Betsy and Miss Lydia were. They never forgot it, and to this day people in Westminster and nearby towns in Maryland tell of the miracle of God's Well and bless Miss Lydia and Miss Betsy for their kind hearts.

Tell a Tale
of Ara Spence

SAID the Terrapin to the Rabbit, "Tell a tale of Ara Spence."

There was no man and there is no man on the eastern shore of Maryland more liked by friends or neighbors than Judge Ara Spence. He had a slithery eel-tongue and could judge near 's good as Solomon; he could tell tales better than a storyteller o' the East an' wasn't afraid of anythin' except our Father in Heaven.

Now, I'm goin' t' tell you a tale about Judge Ara told round Chincoteague Island from where come the finest salty oysters in America, which means the finest oysters in the world.

Judge Ara lived in a fine wooden house right on the shore of Sinepuxet Bay, with many cats, a few cousins, an' many slaves.

There he was in a big house full o' cats an' full o' servants, an' he was mighty kind to both. Most of all he was kind to a little stick of a black boy called Maj, who

274

had glistenin' curly hair, eyes black as the Devil an' just as much trouble-makin', but, no matter what he did, Judge Ara 'd forgive 'm an' just shut his eyes.

He was that kind an' easy, Judge Ara was.

Little Maj, he knew well an' took advantage of the good man night an' day. He ate what he shouldn't, took what he shouldn't, an' never did a lick o' work. The good judge, he'd just smile, say nothin'.

Now, Judge Ara had a fine spyglass used for lookin' at the ships out on the sea, an' he set much on it. Little Maj, he liked that spyglass, too, for playin' with it.

When Judge Ara caught the boy peepin' through his spyglass he told 'm not to touch it or he'd give him a good whippin', but little Maj wasn't scared one bit. He'd heard that often before, an' it never came to pass. So he played with that spyglass when the judge wasn't around.

One day, when the judge had gone away, that little black imp, he took the spyglass an' went out in the garden to look at things. It so happened that Judge Ara came home early that day. He had heaps o' worryment 'bout the British who were fightin' us, as they always did in them days. The enemy ships were anchored in the bay, an' near everybody was scared the sailors 'd come ashore to burn an' rob food an' cattle. The judge went into the garden to figure out on some plans against the Britishers.

Maj spied the judge quick an', fearin' heaps o' trouble, ran off fast 's his legs 'd carry him. He stumbled on a stone, the spyglass fell out o' his hand. Crack! It broke into three pieces!

Judge Ara, he ran up an' saw his prized spyglass all broken an' little Maj sprawlin' on the grass.

Well, the judge was mad 's a man sleepin' in a bean-field, which makes a man mad fit t' kill.

He got hold o' that boy by the ears, dragged 'm up an' shook 'm as if he was goin' shake 'm out of his skin. Little Maj was sure scared this time. The judge hadn't done this ever before.

Then Judge Ara shouted for Maj's father t' come quick. Maj's father, he was Judge Ara's butler man, an' a mighty fine man he was.

Little Maj was lyin' on the grass too scared t' move. The judge 'd never acted up like that before.

The old man came, an' the judge told 'm what that black imp 'd done.

The boy's father couldn't say nothin' because the judge was right.

Judge Ara kept on rantin' an' ravin' some more, an' little Maj, he began losin' his fear. He turned his head a little, lookin' at the judge from the corner of his eye, figurin' he'd get free like he always did. But this one time he bet on the wrong horse.

The judge thought that boy was sassin' him, an' it made him mad 'nuf to eat grass. He shouted to Maj's father:

"Take that good-for-nothin' black imp, tie a rock to 'm, and throw him into the bay."

Little Maj sure thought his end had come. He turned pale, though you couldn't see it; his teeth was clickin', an' he was shakin' all over. He was so scared he was plum paralyzed. Then he cried for no good reason at all:

"Bless Gawd Mass' Ara, don' drown me, I ain't had ma brefas' yit."

Judge Ara had judged for many years an' never had a judgment turned against him. He'd heard many words spoken in them years, but he never heard such words as these. He plum forgot about the Britishers in the bay and forgot Maj had broken his spyglass. He just laughed an' laughed 'bout that little boy wantin' his breakfast before drownin' till tears ran down his face.

He'd've laughed much longer, only Master Prunell, who lived in Mt. Ephraim a little way off, rushed up and cried the British were firin' shots at his home an' gettin' ready t' land.

Judge Ara stopped his laughin', put on his greatcoat, and went out with his neighbor, forgettin' all about little Maj an' what he'd said.

Both were quick a-horse riding swift to Mt. Ephraim.

Judge Ara was feelin' mighty fine, the funny thing little Maj said put him in high spirits. An' when Judge Ara felt high, his head worked faster'n double lightnin'.

"Ha!" he cried, "the British have many ships an' guns an' men, we have only a few, but we'll beat 'em just the same, for what we Marylanders lack in number we'll make up in brains and courage! Friend Prunell, I've an idea that'll trick 'em sure 's persimmons make good wine."

"Friend Ara, we've no guns an' we have only a few soldiers," said Prunell.

"I know, I know that, but I told you we've gray matter in our heads'll make up for the others. Now, listen, here's our plan of action. Ride up an' down the shore an' call out every man, woman, an' child over eight livin' here'bouts. Give as many guns as we have to the men, and to the other men, and to the women, and children give sticks an' have 'em tie shinin' knives at one end so it'll look like gleamin' bayonets. Then we'll arrange 'em in rows of eight abreast an' march 'em up an' down an' all around behind the trees, never stoppin', so it'll look like a great army marchin' round the shore for protection. It'll make the British think twice before landin' to attack us."

Master Prunell sent out the good word, callin' everybody, black an' white, round Mt. Ephraim, Public Landing, Snow Hill, and Watermelon Point. Some came with guns, but most with sticks, knives tied at the end.

Then they formed in rows of eight an' began marchin' up an' down, an' round an' round. They marched behind trees an' behind houses, never in the open, bayonets an' knives flashin' so they could be seen from afar.

The British ridin' at anchor off the coast in the bay were makin' ready to land an' raid the shore when the sailor up in the crow's-nest saw the flash of movin' steel. He called down quick that a big army, hundreds, maybe even thousands, were on the shore.

All them Britishers turned their eyes on the movin' bayonets, movin', flashin' all over the place.

The British captain, he saw them bayonets, too, an'

thought maybe it wasn't so smart to attack such a big force of Americans. Then he thought maybe it was best to get away from a place that had so many soldiers. So off he sailed, an' there was no raid, all thanks to Judge Ara's smartness.

When that boat winged out, Judge Ara, he watched it all the time, for he remembered it said down his way that when you watch a boat sailin' away you'll never see it comin' back.

That's the kind o' stories told 'bout Judge Ara hereabouts. There's many, many more like 'em, an' come some other time, maybe I'll tell you 'nother.

The Spider in the Wall

IN Anne Arundel town in the Queen State of Maryland, there lived a painter named Thomas Murdock, who believed in more foolish things than there are hairs on a hog's back. Silly Tom was the right name for him.

Silly Tom believed in signs and believed in stars, believed in witches and believed in monsters. Believed if he met a cross-eyed man he'd have hard luck and if a horse neighed somebody'd die, and believed if he touched a spider's web at night with his face ghosts followed him all over. And he believed in gold-finding rods, too, and in buried pirates' treasures.

He was always looking for a chest of gold to become rich without working.

One night he walked along the waterfront and met a poor old woman whom people called a witch.

"Good evenin', Mistress," said Thomas Murdock. "Good evenin'. Folks say you're a friend o' the gentleman with the cloven foot. I want to see him. I want to be rich."

"Fool," the woman cried, "fool, there's mud in your head. Just you work honestly at your paintin' every day an' you'll earn enough to live—an' that is all any man needs. If ever you bother me again I'll put a halter on your neck an' ride you to the witch's Sabbath. Then you'll sweat enough to get them crazy notions out o' your head."

She said this only to keep Tom from bothering her, but I told you his head was full of wheezes about witches and riches, so he took her words for gospel and said, "I don't care how you ride me, I'll even rub myself with rabbit's fat as witches do, only lead me where I'll find gold."

"You brainless fool! Out o' my way," she cried, walking off angrily.

Do you think that put any sense in Silly Tom's head? Not a dry straw's worth. Such people never learn, no matter how much you try to teach them.

One evening he walked by the thousand-year-old tulip tree, which all Anne Arundel's townspeople love. The sky was full of clouds running in each other's way, and a ringing wind was making music in the leaves. Along came a man with a piebald horse. Behind walked a black-and-brown dog and a tiny black kitten.

The horse was so high you couldn't see the man's head when you looked from the other side.

"There's the man without the head," cried Tom, his teeth chattering like drumsticks. "Others have seen him, too. He's got a giant horse an' a dog an' a black cat, which is always a bad sign. Maybe it's the Devil walkin'."

He got together all the courage he ever had and cried,

"Ho, there, Master Devil, will you help me find a treasure so that I'll have lots o' money? Just you tell me what you want me to do for helpin', an' I'll gladly do it."

The man with the horse and dog and cat didn't like to be called Devil, and he got mighty mad and shouted, "You nimshi-addled fool! Get out o' my way or I'll send my dog after you an' he'll give you more 'n the Devil."

The dog barked and the cat meowed and the horse neighed.

Tom didn't hear all the words but enough to know the headless man was angry at him, and he thought he'd better run. And while he was running he was thinking, "If witches an' Devil won't help me, then I got to help myself."

Now, Tom Murdock was a painter who liked to paint with white paint only. So he made up a fancy paint, a kind of whitewash that was used mostly on stones. If any man in Anne Arundel town wanted the stones of his house painted, they'd call Tom Murdock to do it.

He'd come and argue for a good price, saying it was a new kind of paint in the land. It was so good that when he put it on a stone it would soak right through the middle and stay on more than a hundred years.

About that time a rich man in a fine house hired Tom Murdock to paint the basement of his house with the white magic paint.

That part of the house was built against the hill in heavy stones and was divided by brick walls and heavy planks into small and large chambers where things were put away. The only light came from narrow windows high up covered with dirt and dust. The rooms looked brown-dark and forbidding, like dungeons in which the ghosts of walled-in women might be living.

Tom came with pots and paints and brushes the very next day and set to work. He painted and he painted till he came to painting a longish chamber that looked like a place where men would hide things they didn't want the light of day to see. There was just one little window high up black with dirt and cobwebs through which came a little light. When Tom came near the window he brushed his face against the cobwebs, and though it wasn't night he was sure some ghost would come his way, just as old folks said.

No sooner did he begin painting than he felt his spine creeping, for he just remembered he'd met a cross-eyed boy that very morning. That meant evil, and he'd forgot to cross himself three times to ward off the spell! He was sure something strange would happen in that chamber.

The little room was silent as a grave save for the queer swishing of the brush and the creaking, wheezy little sounds made by creeping things in the cracks of the stones. He kept on working, the cold sweat running down his back until he reached a big stone that looked different from the others and that had many markings on it.

Tom stopped short, brush in hand, and looked at the stone carefully.

"There's somethin' queer behind that stone," he said

aloud, and the sound of his voice came back to him. "Maybe there's a treasure hid behind that stone. Maybe this was a pirate's hidin' place."

He looked around to make sure no one was there and set to work with his trowel to pry the stone away.

The work was hard, but Tom never noted it; avarice gives a man great strength. He scratched and scraped and scraped and scratched till he loosened the stone, and by prying and pulling hard he got it out and on the floor. Sure enough, there was an empty space behind it.

"There's an iron casket full o' gold in there for sure," Tom cried in red excitement. "Bet it's a treasure hid by some bloody pirate."

He put his hand into the dark empty space and reached as far as he could, but there seemed no end to it. So he put the candle near and stuck his head in and looked all around for a long time. All at once he pulled his head back trembling.

A pair of big, black, bulging eyes were staring at him!

Tom Murdock couldn't move and couldn't speak. He even found it hard to breathe. For out of that opening crawled a creature the like he never dreamed could be.

It was a spider! A spider big as a newborn calf. Each part of that spider was fat and black and round, and his eight long, hairy, dragging legs were black- and yellow-streaked. His mouth was yellow and made the beast look like it came from out of Tophet.

That black fat spider crawled and rolled toward Tom Murdock standing petrified! The long, thin, yellow-and-black hairy legs pulled along the stone floor and made a swishing sound as Tom stood there breathing hard.

Then suddenly Tom lifted the trowel that was in his hand and hit the spider on the head, but it only made a sound like hitting flint and broke the handle in two.

The spider stopped and sort of grinned at Tom, then he opened his jaws showing fangs like sharks' teeth, and Tom picked up his paint brush, lifted it, and threw it at the beast. But the spider caught it in his jaw and crunched the handle into a hundred splinters and just swallowed it like mush.

That was about all Tom Murdock could stand. He lit out faster than a fox with hounds after him.

"Gettin' money from treasures ain't for me," he cried. 'Guess I must stay a painter as the witch woman said."

And a painter he stayed all his life, but he was so silly he never stopped believing in signs and witches.

Adventure in Plaindealing

DOWN in Plaindealing in Maryland they've adventures all their own way.

Every Fourth of July, at midnight, when the trees stretch to look on the dark flowing creek, a great black dog comes slowly along the soft green grass wearily dragging old rusty chains.

Then thick white mists rise from the water and float toward the place where stood the old mansion and the cemetery. The white mists roll and float around the cedars, pines, and weeping willows, and around the beautifully carved tombstones. Suddenly there comes from among them a tall, white lady. She floats slowly around the foundation of the house and then toward the river, disappearing over the water.

To those born in Plaindealing under a lucky star, friendly ghosts will come and show where treasures can be found.

There are other strange tales down in Plaindealing, but the one I want to tell you is a sad, sad story with a nice, nice ending, and it happened a long time ago.

It is a story about Susan of Peach Blossom Mansion, who was married to Thomas of Plaindealing Mansion, and one other—Robert.

Susan and Thomas loved each other as two married people never loved in this world before, they said. They were never out of each other's sight, and the words they spoke were only words of devotion. No one in all Talbot County was happier than these two.

From morn to night they were gay and had parties. In the evening they danced and sang on the green shore of Plaindealing Creek.

But, alas, no man can tell what happens tomorrow, and one day the good Lord took Thomas to Himself, and Susan was left a widow lonesome and forlorn.

She wept and she moaned and she would not eat and she would not drink. She would not talk and she wouldn't do any of the things she used to do, grieving for her husband whom she loved so dearly.

She had a beautiful tombstone carved for Thomas and placed it on his grave in the little graveyard right near and in sight of Plaindealing Mansion. Then she went to her room, from which the cemetery could be seen, placed a chair near the little window, and sat down to look at the tombstone of her dear husband's grave.

She rose early in the morning and sat down in that chair and did not get up until the stars were full in the sky and the trees and the grass were dark and the stone could not be seen.

Day in, day out, week in, week out she did this, and

soon everyone near and dear knew how Susan grieved for her lost husband.

Kith and kin and folks all around begged and argued with her to cease such mourning for the man she loved and whom God had taken unto Himself. But all the pleading and arguing were of little use. It only made her love the dear departed even more.

She never went visiting anyone, she never bade anyone to come to visit her. She sat all the time high up at her little window, looking at the tombstone in the graveyard.

One day Annabelle, the mammy who had known Susan from the day she was born, pleaded with her and said:

"Miss Susan, 'tain't jest natural for a pretty young thing like you to be sittin' the long day, mournin' an' lookin' at a stone, weepin' for what's gone an' can't be brought back. You're young, and you're mighty purty, an' there's many a fine gen'leman be mighty glad t' marry you."

"Hush your mouth, Annabelle, an' don't be saying such things to me any more."

"I ain't sayin' nuffin', Miss Susan, but I know one gen-tleman big 's life and twice 's natural 'd give horn, claws, an' wings if you'd just look at 'm."

"No more o' that, Annabelle, I said. Don't let me hear such talk again. Now, you go an' put a lantern on dear Tom's stone so I can look at it at night even as I do in the day. That's how much I care for other men."

When the word of Susan's new sign of devotion for her

dead Tom spread, folks marveled and said such faithful love was never known in all our land. And gentlemen from Maryland and up as far as Maine and down as far as Florida said Susan was the most perfect and devoted wife that ever was.

So years and years went by, and the story of Susan's faithful love was known everywhere. In the end kith and kin as well as townsfolk were proud to have among them such a wonderful lady.

Seven winters passed, and it was the spring of the seventh year, and still Mistress Susan sat faithfully at the little window, looking at her dear Thomas's tombstone.

It was springtime, when the little leaves come forth and the little flowers raise their heads eagerly in the sweet Maryland winds. That day all life was a-maying and a-wooing, and Annabelle, her face now wrinkled like a spider's web, spoke to Mistress Susan sitting at the window. Said she, as she had said a thousand times before:

"Don't you think, Miss Susan, y've sat there long 'nuf to satisfy Massa Thomas? Ah knows ef he could talk he'd order you take off them widow clothes an' git away offa that window an' go where folks is. 'Tain't good foh you t' be lookin' jest at one thing all the time."

Susan answered as she always did, "Annabelle, I've told you time an' again I love Master Thomas beyond the grave an' I don't wish to do a thing but see his resting place."

"You's plum silly, Miss Susan, an' one day you'll wake

up ol' an' shaky an' gray an' trem'ly jest as I am. An' den . . ."

She stopped, for she saw coming up the roadway a company of gay cavaliers a-horse, and among them one Robert Nichols. He sat on his chestnut mare straight as a cedar, and he stopped in such a way that the tombstone was hidden. Mistress Susan had to look at him. Robert looked straight at the window and saw the lovely widow, a sweet white flower dressed in black with a sad look on her face.

"Mah nose was itchin' in the mornin', an' here's company," said old Annabelle.

Mistress Susan looked down and could not help but see Master Robert, and she looked more than was her wont.

The guests came into the house and were treated right royally, as is the custom in Plaindealing to this very day, but Mistress Susan was not there. She begged to be excused, as she had done the last seven years.

The guests ate and stayed a time and then went their way, but it did not take long before Master Robert came again. He came again and again, and sometimes he and Mistress Susan would talk of things.

It didn't take long, nor did it take short, but one day Master Robert, who was as fine and as quick a gentleman as any, told Mistress Susan what he had in mind, which was that he loved her and would be honored if she would marry him.

Mistress Susan sat looking at the tombstone, as she

always did, when he spoke his words of love. She said she was pleased indeed to have such an honor bestowed on her, but she would have to say no. Master Robert said good-by and added that he would come again.

To that Mistress Susan did not say no, nor did she say yes.

Soon after Master Robert was gone, Annabelle came in.

"Miss Susan," she said, "las' night Ah dreamed Ah saw a fallen star, and when Ah just came acrost the lawn a white kitten crossed mah path. That means good luck, Miss Susan." Then she laughed until her little eyes nearly closed.

"Ah tells you 'gin there's no use wearin' them widow clothes all yoh life."

Mistress Susan sat silently, listening only with one ear to Annabelle's words and with the other ear to the wind talking in the trees and the loblolly pines. They all seemed to say something. Even the perfume of the wild blooming lilac and sweet lilies of the valley coming through the window whispered something. She listened, and she never said a word.

Annabelle looked at her sideways with her wise, old dark eyes and just hummed a little tune.

One day, it was another day when the good Lord made paradise of Plaindealing Mansion in Maryland, Master Robert came up the path again. As he walked up, Annabelle saw in his eyes the glint of a conquering man. In his hand he carried a bunch of lovely heartsease. He went straight to Mistress Susan's chamber, and Annabelle stayed near the door to make sure no one would come in while the two were talking.

They spoke long, they spoke short; some of the words were high, many low, but all mixed together they said and proved to all the world that love for the living is stronger than love for the dead.

That's what a golden oriole singing in a gum tree said, looking at the two, Mistress Susan and Master Robert sitting at the window. I say the same and that is how Mistress Susan stopped looking at the tombstone and looked instead into Master Robert's eyes. The two were married and lived happily ever after.

The Blue Dog

THIS was in the time that's gone by, and I'm goin' to tell you a story 'bout it. In them days there was a skinny peddler from New England, and he traveled till he came way down to Maryland to Port Tobacco by the sea. He came there, him an' his dog.

On his narrow back that peddler carried a pack full of all kind o' notions: white-oak cheeses, calico hog troughs, geese yokes for to fool folks, and he also had things people could buy.

'Twas a cold winter day when he came t' Port Tobacco town, an' young an' old, big an' little, they all followed that peddler man. They followed him quicker than any peddler man they ever followed before t' see his notions an' t' higgle an' haggle for 'em. But they followed him most t' see his dog, 'deed they did. It was a dog the kind had never been seen in Port Tobacco before. It was a dog with blue hair all over! A biggish dog with shaggy hair, blue in the sunlight an' bluer in the moonlight. It trotted behind the peddler like his shadow, an' folks said the Devil sure gave 'm that blue dog, t' help 'm in case anybody tried t' rob him.

Come night, a big storm blew up, an' the Yankee peddler went to the St. Charles Inn, where he drank punch an' persimmon beer more than's good for a man an' spoke more 'n is good for a man. On top o' that he boasted loud 'bout his bag full o' gold an' opened it wide, right near the fireplace so's it could be seen gleamin' an' glitterin' in the yellow light.

Now, there was in the inn right then three black scallawags, the kind wouldn't stop at anythin', an' when they saw that shinin' gold their eyes bulged like bullfrogs. They went off by themselves, whisperin', an' then two of 'em went from out the lighted room into the black night, an' one stayed behind.

The one that stayed behind got to talkin' to the skinny peddler man kind o' friendly, an' when closin' time came an' the storm had died he said there was a fine place near Rose Hill house where they could stop for the night.

The two went out together. A thin sliver of a moon shone in the sky of racin' clouds, an' a jumpy wind was runnin' round the trees scoldin' an' cryin'.

The peddler an' the man, they walked along till they came to a dark lane goin' up to Rose Hill house.

They walked till they came to a big rock, when two men sprang from the bushes and attacked the peddler man while the one that had walked beside him hit the dog a fierce clout on the head. That was the end o' both of 'em.

They took the peddler's bag full o' gold, but instead o' dividin' it they buried it a ways off, figurin' they'd take it after people 'd forget about the foul murder. Then they sneaked off, leavin' the dead man an' the dead blue dog on the road. To this day y' can see the red blood on the round rock where the crime was done. No water from heaven kin wash it off, 'deed it can't.

The next mornin' folks found the dead peddler an' his dead dog but never a sign of his gold. So they buried the two in the cool earth under a tall buttonwood tree.

The three murderers, they waited till folks talked no more 'bout the crime an' came t' git the gold.

That night there was a sliver of a moon in the sky o' racin' clouds an' a jumpy wind ran roun' the trees scoldin' an' cryin'.

The three murderers walked along the dark paths, not sayin' much, for they felt kind o' jumpy themselves.

They got 'bout halfway up the hill when they heard a long yippidy howlin', an' quick after came rushin' between the trees a dog—with blue hair tousled an' tumbled all over. The blue dog! The blue dog of the murdered peddler! Its jaws were wide open an' the red tongue hangin' way out. It was the peddler's blue dog, sure 'nuf.

First the murderers couldn't move, they was so full o' witch fears an' their hearts thumpin' like hammers. Then one of 'em got his legs back an' began runnin' like the plague was after 'm. Before you could squinch an eyeball the other two followed. They ran an' they stumbled an' they stumbled an' they ran, followed by the howlin' o' that blue dog, till they came to Rose Hill house. There they tol' they'd seen a ghost, but they didn't tell they'd

seen the ghost of the blue dog that belonged to the Yankee peddler for fear they'd be questiond too much.

From then on other folks heard an' saw the blue dog
round Rose Hill house. Sometimes it seemed as if the dog
was tryin' to lead 'em where the gold was hid, but no
man dared to follow 'm.

Sometimes that blue ghost dog 'd be barkin' when some
trouble 'd come to those in Rose Hill house.

One day a black man came tremblin' with white fear,
tellin' he'd seen the blue ghost dog comin' straight from
the sky in a cloud o' smoke an' thunder just like 'Lija the
prophet. Sure 'nuf, someone in Rose Hill house died soon
after.

Folks said if you sat on the bloody rock till midnight,
mostly in the month o' February, and wasn't scared when
the blue dog came rushin' up, an' followed him, hc'd lead
you to where the treasure was hid. But everybody was
scared o' that ghost animal. 'Deed, sir, they was. Said the
Devil himself was inside the blue skin o' that dog.

So the wheel o' time run along, an' summers an' winters come an' passed, but there was one thing that didn't
pass, an' that was that blue ghost dog round Rose Hill
house.

Came the great war, the sad war. In them days little
Miss 'Livia Floyd lived in Rose Hill house.

That Miss 'Livia wasn't scared of anythin' walkin',
flyin', or creepin', not even General Hooker an' the Yankee soldiers billeted in Rose Hill house an' nearby. She

carried two mother-o'-pearl pistols in her belt an' knew how to use 'em.

The general always made fun o' Miss 'Livia, said she carried them pistols for fear o' that blue ghost dog everybody was scared of. He an' his Yankee soldiers heard all 'bout the blue dog an' the treasure o' gold that was never found.

Miss 'Livia, she told him quick 'nuf she wasn't scared o' no blue dogs and no blue-clad Yankees neither. She just carried them pistols in case she had need of 'em.

One morning the Yankee general said he had t' go some place on war business.

"An' what am I goin' to do with your Yankee soldiers in case they don't behave?" asked Miss Floyd.

"They'll behave," said the Yankee general. "Besides, I reckon a lady carryin' mother-o'-pearl pistols can well take care of herself. You just use 'em if you have to."

He went away on his war business, leavin' the woman with the soldiers.

The next night when there was a sliver of a moon shinin' in a sky o' racin' clouds an' a jumpy wind was runnin' round the trees scoldin' an' cryin', two o' them Yankee soldiers thought it was a fittin' time t' git the Yankee peddler's gold.

They sneaked off without bein' seen, each one carryin' a spade, an' soon came alongside the hill where folks said the gold was hid. When they was gittin' near the spot they heard a murderous long yowlin' an' yelpin'. Well, they was soldiers carryin' pistols, so they wasn't too much scared first. They kept on lookin' an' pokin' an' diggin' with their spades in different places.

The howlin' kept on gittin' worser an' worser all the time, an' pretty soon they saw by the light o' the yellow moon a biggish dog with shaggy blue hair rushin' through the trees just like a ghost. His head was high an' jaws wide open, an' he stared with his glassy eyes all round, yowlin', yelpin' all the time. All the time. That was a sight 'd even scare a general. They dropped their spades an' just ran off like foxes with hounds after 'em. They never stopped till they come t' Rose Hill with its sharp-smellin' box-wood hedges, and there they told the tale to the other soldiers.

Some believed an' some didn't, but all were a little scared, 'deed they were. An' since the best way to take scare away from the stomach is by fillin' it full, they figured if they could only git a few chickens from Miss 'Livia's hen-house they wouldn't be no more scared o' blue dogs or gray uniforms.

So two o' them soldiers went to the chicken-house, where Miss 'Livia had some fine chickens, t' get one of 'em for roastin'. When they got 'mongst the fowls they raised such a rumpus you could hear 'em plum to the other end o' Maryland.

They clucked an' screeched so loud, Miss 'Livia, sittin' in the great room by the fireside with the beautiful carved mantel, thought sure a fox had gotten in that hen-house. She was a right smart little woman an' unafeared of anythin'. So she jumped up, took her two pearly-han-

dled pistols, an' ran to the hen-house. When she opened
the door she saw by the light o' the yellow moon the two
Yankee soldiers tryin' t' catch a chicken.

Miss 'Livia, she stood at the door an' leveled her two
pistols, one in each hand, straight at them Yankee soldiers and said, "You leave my chickens alone, you Yankees, or I'll put you in the hottest place you ever was
before you kin say grace."

Well, them soldiers stood there, mouths wide open,
lookin' at the little lady with the pistols in her hand. Then
they walked out kind o' sheepish-lookin' an' went back
to their quarters an' told what had happened. Right then
Yankee General Hooker came in an' heard all the tale;
'bout the treasure hunt an' the chicken hunt.

He said nothin' for a time, then he got up an' said,
"Guess we better not tamper with things in a place where
blue ghost dogs watch the gold an' ladies with mother-o'-
pearl pistols guard the houses."

And that's just what they did long as they stayed in
Rose Hill house.

But to this day, when there's a sliver of a moon in the
sky an' a jumpy wind is runnin' wildly roun' the trees,
scoldin' an' cryin', folks say y' kin hear the blue ghost
dog howlin' an' yelpin'. An' y' can see him rushin' between the trees an' brush tryin' to show you where the
Yankee peddler's treasure's hid. If you got courage an'
follow that blue dog y' kin get the gold. I didn't and
never got it, 'deed I didn't.